American Indian Tales and Legends

American Indian

by VLADIMÍR HULPACH

Illustrated by
MILOSLAV TROUP

Tales and Legends

PAUL HAMLYN · LONDON

Translated by George Theiner
Illustrated by Miloslav Troup
Graphic design by Oldřich Hlavsa
First published 1965
Second impression 1966

Designed and produced by Artia
Published by Paul Hamlyn
Drury House ● Russell Street ● London WC2
for Golden Pleasure Books Ltd
© 1965 by Artia
Printed in Czechoslovakia by Svoboda, Prague
S 1964

CONTENTS

ONCE UPON A TIME, in the days of our forefathers, when peace still reigned in the lands of the American Indians and the ships of the pale-faces had not yet appeared on the far horizon of the Great Water, the Great Spirit invited the chieftains of all the powerful tribes to gather around the camp-fire. He then ordered the animals to make ready the camp site and bring wood for the fire.

The bear and the bison dragged the heaviest trunks, the caribou cut them up into logs with his sharp-pointed horns, while the wolverene stacked them on top of each other. Even the squirrel did his best to help, running about the forest and picking up every twig he found. The rabbit was a comic sight, bringing dry grass from the prairie; the grass either stuck out of his mouth on all sides so that he looked just like the wandering otter, Talagwa, or it hung limply on his chin like the beard of the grumpy mountain goat.

The most important work the Great Spirit reserved for himself. Sitting down in his wigwam above the clouds, he thoroughly examined the stones and clay brought to him from every corner of the country inhabited by the Indians. Some he threw away, some he kept. Finally he drew a deep

breath and blew. The clay and the stones crumbled into a fine dust. Wetting his fingers several times in the rivers and lakes, the Great Spirit began to recite a spell, while his hands started shaping the magic pipe, or calumet.

When only a small crescent was lacking to the full moon the Great Spirit finished his work and descended to earth. Just then came the brave chieftain of the Dakotas. He recognised the Great Spirit and stood still, overcome with awe.

'Have no fear, chieftain of a brave people, but approach nearer!' the Great Spirit said to him. 'I have brought a gift to your camp-fire: this magic calumet. It will memorise all the words spoken here today, and will repeat them to anyone who questions it, no matter how many years hence. I want you therefore to fill your mouths with every wisdom about the world and its ways, about animals and people and their actions. And now take the sacred pipe from me.'

As soon as the chieftain had taken the calumet, the Great Spirit vanished like smoke in the evening breeze.

The Sun went to sleep, sending its sister, the Moon, up into the sky in its place. When the

Moon had spread its glittering veil over the countryside, a fire was kindled on the plain where the mountains meet the prairie and the snow-covered forests join the arid desert; the fire crackled and lit up the proud, wise faces of the Indians with a golden glow.

It was surely the biggest camp-fire ever to be lit in the country of the Indians. The flames sprang higher than the tree-tops and, indeed, some of them seemed to reach as far as the sky. The chieftains of all the tribes sat in a large circle round the fire: those from the forests of eternal snow clad in furs, the warriors from the South bronzed by the Sun, and the hunters from the prairies wearing magnificent head-dresses.

And as the Moon in its soft moccasins crossed the night sky, the calumet was passed from mouth to mouth, carefully committing to memory every single word of the ancient legends told by the assembled Indians.

A new day was born — the fire had gone out and the chieftains dispersed to return to their homes. Only the calumet remained.

Since then the ice-floes passed down the rivers in the North and the prairie flowered many times. Many wars came and went, and in the end the pale-faces drove the Indians out of their ancient hunting-grounds.

The magic calumet was completely forgotten. It lay, battered, in the dust by the wayside and no one bothered even to look at it.

But one day a small boy happened to be playing near it, and he was so intrigued by the strange-looking object that he took it home with him. There he kept cleaning and polishing it until it was just like new again.

Evening came. The boy's father set fire to the pitch-pine logs in the fireplace, and the room filled with the smell of resin and with strange, fairy-tale shadows. The calumet lay on the table, and the boy watched it with curious eyes. He had a feeling it was no ordinary pipe. And, true enough, all of a sudden the calumet moved as if coming awake after a long sleep, emitted an almost imperceptible whiff of smoke, and began to speak in a low, soothing voice. . . .

The First
Light

Even before the oldest legend began — a legend which I have been told by the animals — Mother Earth was under the spell of the Big Sleep. The world was lost in darkness, enveloped in it as if it had been swamped by one great black wave; not a single sound interrupted the profound silence.

Perhaps the Earth would never have awakened at all, had it not been for the white cloud. It so happened that the white cloud opened its eyes and, seeing nothing but darkness, left its home in the North and slowly travelled eastwards, cautiously finding its way.

It soon met with danger. A terrible black cloud hovered in the east, the guardian of the Big Sleep, who alone could penetrate the pitch-black darkness and who was constantly on the alert, watching for any untoward movement. As soon as it caught sight of the white cloud groping and struggling across the sky, it bristled like a wildcat and flew forward to punish the trespasser.

They clashed right above the Indian country. The black cloud leapt upon its white brother and started to shower it with blows. The white cloud did not give way, but stood up to the attack.

Only Manitou knows how this encounter would have ended, but just then a strange, unprecedented thing happened: as the two clouds fought, their sweat began to pour, and the drops joined up, one with the other, until at last it began to rain.

The rain brought life to the Indian country. The animals came running out from under the ground, where they had been imprisoned by the Big Sleep. The water, pouring down from heaven, made a hole in the earth through which they all clambered out.

And now it seemed that they would all live in peace and happiness. They divided the hunting-grounds among themselves, from the big plains right across the mountains and canyons, all the way to the frontier of the Snow Country, and before long each creature was building its own home. But something was still lacking in the world, something no one yet had ever seen. The light! During the Big Sleep the spirits had carried it away, and consequently the whole world was in darkness.

Luckily a small remnant of the little white cloud was still up there in the sky. It was so tired after its great fight that it could hardly move, but it called its friends, the blue cloud and the yellow cloud.

The blue cloud lived far away at the southern end of the world while the yellow cloud had its home in the West. They both woke up and came hurrying towards the white cloud as fast as the wind could carry them.

'The world has risen from the Big Sleep,' explained the white cloud by way of welcome. 'Now it needs some light, and that is why I have decided to call you in to help me. Let us light up the Indian country.'

'Oh, but we shall soon feel fatigued,' protested the blue cloud.

'I don't think I can stay in one place for any length of time,' added the yellow cloud.

'Don't worry — our light is feeble and will hardly satisfy anyone. Soon we shall be wandering about the sky as the fancy takes us.'

His friends made no further protest. Coming down as low as they could, they shone their coloured lamps on the earth with all their might. In this way there was at last a little light in the world, but the animals knew well enough that they were now faced with their first difficult task: to bring *real* light.

Who Brought the Sun?

In those days, as we have seen, neither the Sun nor the Moon shone upon the earth. No one succeeded in doing anything because no one could see in the dark— only the owl was able to light its way with its eyes.

The coyote grew thin, for although he went hunting every day, he never managed to catch any rabbits, and in the end had to make do with an occasional grasshopper to soothe the pangs of hunger for a while. Then he would sit dejectedly in front of his den, looking round with hungry eyes.

Suddenly he heard the swish of mighty wings. The eagle had come to pay him a visit. The coyote bent his back and bowed, saying:

'Ah, what an unexpected honour! Welcome, brother. I wish I could offer you something, but I haven't so much as a gnawed bone. I am quite famished myself and can hardly walk any more. You, l am sure, are much better off. How I wish I could go hunting with you!'

The eagle looked the coyote up and down, thinking. 'He looks like a scarecrow, nothing but skin and bone.'

'Well, we can always try,' he said. 'But you must help me.'

'Oh, yes, yes, anything you say!' cried the coyote, embracing the eagle with his emaciated paws and almost choking him for joy.

The next day they set out hunting together. The eagle circled high up in the air and as soon as he sighted his prey, he plunged headlong to the ground. The coyote did not catch anything, nor did he try to — he was quite satisfied with sharing the eagle's booty.

'I have no need of such a worthless assistant!' exclaimed the eagle. 'You don't even bother to bury the bones — you simply leave them scattered on the ground.'

'How can I help it? It's so dark I can't see the tip of my nose,' protested the coyote. 'What we need is some light.'

'True enough,' agreed the eagle. 'I've heard that far away to the west two big lights are hidden; one is called the Sun and the other the Moon. Let's go there and we are sure to find them.'

They soon started on their journey. They walked and walked (or rather, the coyote did, for the eagle flew in the air) until they came to a wide river. The eagle waved its wings and flew across, settling on the opposite bank. The coyote remained standing indecisively in front of the muddy water, feeling little inclination to jump in. Nevertheless, he did. His head bobbed up and down on the surface, his eyes bulging as he paddled with all four paws at once.

As soon as he felt the firm ground beneath him again he cried angrily:

'I almost drowned and you sit here as if nothing had happened. Why didn't you carry me across?'

'Why don't you grow feathers? You could have flown across like me if you had feathers.' And the eagle ruffled his plumage with loving care.

'Idiot!' the coyote spluttered with rage. 'I'd like to see what you would have done in my place!'

But he knew it would not be wise to annoy the eagle, so he stopped complaining, and they set off once more.

The country round them gradually changed in character, the outlines of isolated hills and cliffs becoming more and more distinct. They were approaching the light. All of a sudden the eagle changed course, circling lower and lower. The coyote quickly ran up a low hillock which hindered his view and saw, in a large clearing below, a number of strange creatures jumping about and dancing and singing. They were all so hideously painted that his hairs stood on end with horror.

'Quiet!' the eagle, who had landed next to the coyote, warned him. 'These are *katchinas*, evil spirits.'

'W-w-won't they h-h-hurt us?' stammered the coyote, his teeth chattering with fear.

'There's no need to be afraid — they don't know we're here. You see those two chests over there?' The eagle pointed into the midst of the yelling dancers. Every now and again one of them would open the lid of one the chests, whereupon a brilliant shaft of light illuminated the clearing.

'What's that?' the coyote asked.

'In one of the chests they have hidden the Sun, in the other, the Moon,' explained the eagle.

'And do you really think we will manage to . . . ?'

'We must wait until the *katchinas* go to sleep. Only you must stop shivering like this all the time.'

The coyote hid his head between his paws, so afraid was he of the evil spirits.

The dance came to an end at last — overcome with fatigue, the *katchinas* dropped off one by one, and soon they were all snoring so loudly that the rocks reverberated with the noise.

This was the moment the two animals were waiting for: the eagle pounced on the chests, dropping down like an arrow, and, seizing them in his claws, vanished in the clouds. The coyote ran for all he was worth, sweeping the ground with his tail.

He did not dare to look round until he was over the first hill; there was no one pursuing them, the *katchinas* slept like logs and had no idea what had happened.

'I wonder what the Sun looks like?' said the coyote to himself. 'And the Moon? That must be particularly beautiful. I really ought to take a peep at them.'

He lifted his head and called out to the eagle:

'Aren't you tired yet, brother?'

But the eagle only laughed and called back from his height:

'That's nothing — I can easily carry them the rest of the way.'

'Oh, but surely it is not fitting for the eagle, the animal chieftain, to be carrying loads.'

'Never mind. I do not stand on ceremony.'

'Oh, but what would the others say if they saw you toiling hard like this? In the end they'll blame me for it, that's what they'll do,' the coyote persisted. He begged and pleaded, inventing all sorts of things to make the eagle let him carry the chests so that he could satisfy his curiosity.

'All right, then,' said the eagle finally, setting the chests down on the ground. 'But you must be very careful with them.' And he again soared up into the air.

When the eagle had come to rest on top of the nearest mountain, the coyote could no longer restrain himself and slowly lifted the lid of the large chest.

'Oh, how marvellous!' he exclaimed. 'What warmth, what golden radiance! I must warm my hands a little.' And he stuck his paws inside the chest.

'Ouch! I'm burned!' he cried suddenly, throwing the lid open in his confusion. Before he could do anything about it, the Sun had jumped out, whoosh! and in one leap had reached the sky. The coyote implored it to come back, clasping his scorched paws together, but the Sun mounted higher and higher and paid no heed to his entreaties.

'I must send the Moon to fetch the Sun back,' it occurred to him. He therefore opened the lid of the second chest.

But the Moon was as merciless as the Sun had been before it. It climbed up to the sky and hid in the Sun's shadow.

The coyote paced up and down by the empty chests, fearfully looking out for the eagle. The big bird arrived soon and scolded him:

'Now look what you've done! Instead of eternal light, there will be night and day succeeding each other all the time, only because you let the Sun get away.'

The coyote hung his head guiltily.

'I'm sorry, I didn't realise . . .' he said meekly. 'But at least the *katchinas* can't take the Sun back either.'

'There's something in that, when you come to think of it,' admitted the eagle. 'Anyway you'd better keep the whole thing to yourself, for no one would be likely to believe you.'

And, waving his wings in farewell, the eagle made for the mountains.

The coyote ran off to his home in the prairie, whistling merrily and looking round to the right and to the left as never before. You see, at that moment the first day had just been born in the Indian country.

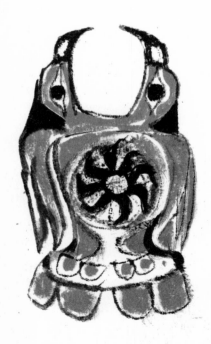

The Fire Myth

The Sun's rays spread all over the Indian country, but they did not reach Deep Valley. There, harsh winter still reigned supreme, and all the animals, with the sole exception of the bear with his thick, shaggy coat, were completely at its mercy.

One night a dreadful storm broke, bending and uprooting trees, shattering rocks, destroying everything that stood in its way. Yet on a small islet in the middle of the Great Water there stood a solitary sycamore, quite unconcernedly singing a song about summer and making fun of the seething elements.

This infuriated the storm still further.

'I'll kill you!' shouted the thunder, striking directly at the heart of the brave sycamore.

Wonder of wonders — even now the song did not cease. The fire in the heart of the sycamore passed it on to the waves of the lake, and these in turn conveyed the song to the shores, and from there it flew farther afield.

The storm had spent itself by now. It was almost dawn, and the storm went away towards the north, leaving havoc behind. The thunder tripped alongside, looking round all the time at the stricken sycamore.

The tree sang no more. Its trunk and its branches were consumed with fire, and a column of blue smoke rose up to the heavens.

The animals in Deep Valley soon noticed the smoke.

The falcon flew high up into the air and gazed in its direction.

'Fire!' he called down. 'There's a fire on the island!'

'What does this fire look like?' asked the other animals.

'It's red and yellow, and it is singing,' replied the falcon. 'But that's all I know about it.'

'Fire is our friend,' said the spider. 'If we bring it here, it will keep us warm. Do you want me to go and fetch it?'

'What, you?' laughed the owl mockingly. 'Your legs are so crooked, it would take you a bear's sleep to go and return. I shall go myself.'

And the owl fluttered her wings and quickly made off towards the island.

Bringing the fire proved to be a much more difficult job than she had imagined. When she found the burning ember she cried out in pain and dropped it. She had singed her

feathers and was glad to get home without any more trouble. Sitting disconsolately on a bough, she apologised:

'The fire doesn't want to have anything to do with us. It didn't even deign to speak to me and it all but killed me.'

'I have a tough skin,' boasted the rattlesnake. 'I'll go and see what I can do.'

But he, too, was quickly driven back by the burning pain inflicted by the fire.

'The fire has extraordinary powers,' he explained to the others when he had returned empty-handed. 'It burned me all over, turning me red. No one will ever make it leave its island.'

'Have you forgotten me?' exclaimed the spider. 'I also have extraordinary powers and, who knows, maybe I'll succeed in bringing the fire. I know how to handle it.'

Though hardly anyone believed him, none of the animals jeered any more; they were all curious to see if he would fulfil his promise.

The spider was in no hurry to start. First, he fetched a huge bundle and, tying it carefully, threw it on his back. Then he set off on his way to the island.

The journey took him a long time. His crooked legs had great difficulty with the various obstacles, and when he entered the water the waves flung him hither and thither, and it was all he could do to prevent his bundle from pulling him down to the bottom. He was glad indeed to reach the island and climb out of the water.

He had a brief rest and then set to work with a will. Out of his bundle he took a very long thread and, bit by bit, entwined the hottest ember with it, dancing a magic spider dance as he did so, to prevent the fire from burning the thread. When he had finished, he put his precious booty in the bundle and started out on his return journey.

All the animals were waiting for him impatiently, and they flocked round, eager to see how he had fared. The spider shook the fire out of his bundle, saying:

'The brave sycamore has sent us a friend who gives heat even in the most bitter of frosts. But we must look after him and feed him, or he will grow cold.'

'I hope he won't eat too much,' said the hamster, afraid that he might be asked to give up his store of food.

'Don't worry,' the spider reassured him, 'the fire only eats dry wood.'

'Oh, but there has been a storm and all the wood is damp!'

'I'll give the fire my bark. That will burn even though it's wet,' said the birch, throwing down a large piece of white bark. The squirrel tore off a strip and held it against the ember. A yellow-red tongue of flame shot up, growing larger and larger and chasing away the cold.

Since then the fire has never gone out. The squirrel tended it in the daytime, while in the evening all the animals gathered round it, singing a song which you can also hear the flames sing if you listen very carefully:

'*When the flames burn bright and clear,*
We gather round and then we hear
The leaves singing their song without end:
That the warm, bright fire is always our friend.'

The Big Flood

Once in the winter — the world was very young and inexperienced in those days — it began to snow heavily. Flake after flake fell from the sky, and the countryside changed beyond all recognition. The snow covered the familiar paths, swept down into the valleys, and blotted out the rivers.

The animals sat round the fire inside a tent made of hides, debating among themselves how to bring the warm weather back. But no one could think of anything. Finally the squirrel said:

'Night is approaching — the fire sings no more, for it is tired. Let us go to bed; we shall all be able to think more clearly in the morning.'

Most of the animals really did go to sleep. The squirrel lay down next to the fire, supported her chin on her paws and, rocked by the waves of heat from the fire and by gusts of wind, she had a strange dream:

She dreamed that a bear was going about the world — a bear just like the one who lived on the other side of the lake — and he was putting everything he could find in a huge sack. In it he had mushrooms, bumble-bee honey, and fine weather. All that had to be done was to take the sack from the bear and open it. . . .

Hastily the squirrel rubbed her eyes, so as to make sure she did not forget her dream.

'Get up, all of you!' she shouted. 'I know who has taken the fine weather from us!'

Her voice roused even the badger, who was well known for his ability to sleep at all times; he sat up and listened attentively.

'I had a dream in which I saw the bear hide it in his sack!' cried the squirrel in great excitement. 'We must run and catch him.'

'Let's cross the lake in the canoe,' suggested the fox.

They all rushed out of the wigwam, launched their canoe, and were off without delay.

The bear's den seemed deserted. They waited a long time, listening carefully, but all was silence inside.

The squirrel was the first to look in, and she cried out for joy: the sack stood there in a corner, just as she had seen it in her dream. She called out to the others:

'Come and help me!'

The sack was very heavy and only the caribou could move it. He picked it up and put it in their canoe.

'The bear is sure to find out what's happened and will come after us,' said the fox. 'Which of you has the sharpest teeth?'

'I have, I!' someone cried in a shrill little voice.

'You, mouse?'

'Yes, I have the sharpest teeth of all,' said the mouse proudly.

'All right, you go and gnaw through the bear's paddle. But do it so that he doesn't notice anything.'

The mouse set to work at once, making a hole in the paddle at the place where it broadened out.

'Hurry, hurry!' the other animals called, for they could hear the bear approaching, grunting as he went.

The mouse did not have time to finish the job. Hearing a heavy footfall outside the cave, she hurried out and jumped into the canoe.

They had only gone a short distance from the shore when an angry roar reached their ears — the bear had discovered the theft.

'You wait till I catch you!' he shouted after them. He picked up his paddle, threw his canoe into the water as if it were a mere shell, and paddled furiously, gaining on them with every stroke. One more lunge and he would have caught up with them — but just then the paddle broke in two, the canoe tipped, and the bear fell into the water and was drowned.

The animals were greatly relieved. When they reached their side of the lake, the caribou carried the sack ashore and carefully untied it.

The fine weather jumped out at once and ran about the countryside. The snow melted quickly, and soon there was water everywhere — all the brooks and rivers joined up in one big stream which came flooding into the valleys. The lake overflowed its banks, and the waters overran everything that stood in the way. All the animals sought refuge on top of a high mountain which alone remained dry.

The deluge spread and only the summit still stood out above the surface. The animals discussed what should be done. They hoped that perhaps the water might gradually recede, but it did not do so.

'I'll dive down and bring up some earth,' suggested the otter. 'Otherwise we'll all perish here.'

The otter took a very deep breath and disappeared under the water. He did not come back for a long time. Then at last he broke surface and, spitting and spluttering, reported.

'Sorry, but I couldn't find the bottom. Let someone else have a try.'

The pike volunteered to go; he spent an even longer time in the water, but was no more successful than the otter.

Then it was the duck's turn. She dived in and went down like a stone. The journey seemed endless, and she was about to turn back when she suddenly touched bottom. Scooping up as much earth as she could, the duck quickly returned to the surface.

True, she did not bring back any great quantity of earth on her webbed feet, but at least she knew the way now and could lead the others. Thus the animals soon brought the whole Indian country out from under the water, and they returned to their homes, having triumphed over the big flood.

How the Indians
Came into
the World

You will be thinking by now that in this tale of mine about the Indian country I have forgotten all about the Indians. But no; I haven't forgotten. In those ancient days they were still living in the region above the clouds and had no inkling of what went on in the world below.

They had everything they needed, their only worry being to find a nice, round, puffy cloud which would rock them from morning till nightfall and from nightfall till morning.

People, however, are a very discontented lot, and there were some who felt dissatisfied even with this tranquil existence above the clouds. They began to wonder why it was that the Sun only retired to its wigwam overnight. What did it do throughout the day?

The bravest of them, Shagodyoweg, sent scouts to follow the burning disc. Then he called together the hunters.

'We'll set a huge trap and catch the Sun,' he told them. 'Tell your squaws to make a strong rope out of the fuzzy clouds, so that we have something to bind it with.'

Shagodyoweg's plan did not meet with general approval, though. Some did not even bother to lift their heads from the papers and books they kept writing, while others only muttered something about the crazy ideas some people have, and went away.

Even so Shagodyoweg found quite a few supporters. And the scouts were back already with a piece of good news.

The Sun's path was long, it led right to the very end of the sky. There, it always disappeared inside a huge opening, which gave off a smell of burning. That was the most suitable place for their trap!

It took them the best part of a day to set the trap among the clouds. It was a far more difficult job than it would have been on the ground, where a sizeable stone would have sufficed to hold it in place; as it was, they had to bring large piles of cloud and drive away the mischievous wind to prevent it from carrying off the snare.

Thus it happened that the hunters only took up their positions when the Sun was nearing the opening. Its rays, which at first were as pleasant as the touch of soft furs, began to scorch their faces. The heat soon became unbearable, yet not one of the hunters left his post. The Sun came nearer and nearer. . . .

Crash! The trap was sprung with a deafening noise. The hunters rushed in with the swiftness of lightning, and before the giant knew what had happened, he was firmly bound.

Realising that he was trapped, he flew into a great rage, furiously tugging at the rope and belching fire on all sides. But he was helpless.

Shagodyoweg urged on his warriors, and women and children came running up to help them, everyone pulling and hauling at the rope.

The Sun was beside himself with rage. The sky rocked from side to side. Now the trap gave way, and the fight began in earnest. They fell and scrambled to their feet again, and the sky reared like a mustang.

Several cowardly souls, pale with fright, were still cowering on one of the clouds, hiding behind their papers. Suddenly one of them seized a hoe and struck at the sky. There was a sharp report, lightning flashed, and the hunters as well as the Sun toppled over and began to fall towards the earth.

The pale-faces breathed a sigh of relief. Picking up their scattered papers, they settled themselves comfortably on the clouds and started to read as though nothing had ever happened.

In the meantime Shagodyoweg and his friends hung from the sky, suspended on the long rope with which they had meant to tie up the Sun, and they were convinced their last hour had come.

But the Sun, great warrior that he was, showed mercy.

'You have fought most valiantly,' he said, 'even in the fierce heat which coloured your skin red. In return, I'll give you a country which will bear your name, the name of the brave redskins, the Indians.'

As the Sun spoke, Shagodyoweg felt the rope sag; he sank lower and lower, until he landed softly in the moss. The others followed, one by one.

When the last Indian had come down to earth, Shagodyoweg, the first chieftain, rose and made this memorable speech:

'My eyes see the most beautiful of lands. Go and pitch your tents in it, light fires, and treat each other and all fellow creatures as brothers. The greater the number of your fires, the more hospitable will the land become, the firmer the bonds of your brotherhood, and the mightier your strength. Woe to you, though, should you let those fires go out. Then even a mere handful of craven pale-faces would easily outwit you, as has happened before.'

The Indians were careful to remember the wise counsel of their chieftain, and they frequently repeated it to their children, as well as the story of how the Indians came to settle in their country. And the children passed on the word of their fathers, from generation to generation, until the tale became a legend, which has come down through the ages to me, and now to you.

The White
Trail
in the Sky

No one can remember any more exactly how it came about that the black bear Wakini overpowered the strong grey grizzly Wakinu. The black bears say that Wakini was just feeding on the contents of an ant-hill when Wakinu came up to him and quite rudely stuck his paw in as well. A great fight ensued, with grey and black hairs flying on every side. Wakini was, of course, in the right, for no animal may ever touch another's prey.

Wakinu thus received a just punishment; but that was by no means all — like a defeated warrior, he had to leave his tribe forever.

Wakinu wailed and lamented, but the Indian laws are inexorable. And so he had to go, wading through familiar streams, taking a last look at the familiar pines, and saying farewell to the valley he had lived in all his life.

He could not see for tears, and so he failed to notice that he was making straight for the Snow Country. Suddenly he fell into a deep snowdrift. Clambering out with difficulty, he wiped his eyes and took a look round.

There was nothing but white, unblemished snow everywhere.

'I'm sure to find a trail soon,' the bear said to himself, and set out on his way once more. His grey coat had turned completely white with the snow, ice, and bitter wind.

But Wakinu took no notice of anything and walked on and on, until he reached a strange land in which a deep, frosty night reigned supreme. Somewhere in the far distance the gale could still be heard, yet here there was no sound but that made by his own footfalls on the frozen snow.

Above him glowed the night sky, while not far away, on the very fringe of the Snow Country and the heavens, a broad white trail could be seen ascending the sky.

Wakinu ran, hardly touching the ground, mesmerised by that gleaming trail. Another leap, and he found himself in the air, shaking the snow from his coat; light as a feather, he soared up and up.

The animals who were awake that night saw, for the first time, a wide white trail in the sky, and on it — a grey bear.

'Wakinu has found the Bridge of Dead Souls and is on his way to the Eternal Hunting-grounds,' said the wise black bear Wakini.

And the grizzly really did go to the Eternal Hunting-grounds. The only thing he left behind was the snow he had shaken from his coat. And that white snow is there in the sky to this day. Just look and see!

The pale-faces speak about the Milky Way, but every Indian knows that that is the way to the Eternal Hunting-grounds, the path taken by the grey grizzly Wakinu.

The Rainbow Snake

Whenever the rainbow makes its appearance in the sky, everyone who sees it is astonished by its many colours and wants to know where all this unusual beauty has come from. It is only the Indians in the west who know and tell an ancient legend that explains how the rainbow came to be in the sky.

It was at a time of stifling heat; the hot air quivered over the arid prairie, the lakes and rivers dried up, and the people, trying to shelter in the shade, lamented:

'Alack, we're bound to perish!'

'All the game is going away in search of water.'

'The fish are moving downstream.'

'Not even the roses will give us their seeds to eat, for they will all wither and wilt.'

A small scaly snake overheard their lamentation. Coming out of his hiding-place, he spoke to them in a human voice, much to their surprise:

'I have great magic powers, and I shall help you. All you need to do is throw me up to the sky.'

'But you're sure to fall down and be killed,' said the Indian shaman, for the shaman was thought to have the greatest magic powers, and he did not believe the snake.

'No, I shan't,' replied the snake. 'I'll hold on to the sky with my scales, and I'll use them to scratch some rain and snow for you, since the meadows up there are made of blue ice.'

'But you're far too small,' the shaman protested again.

'I can stretch myself across the whole horizon,' the snake replied. 'Go on, just throw me as high as you can.'

The shaman said no more but, picking up the coiled snake, hurled it up towards the cloudless sky with all the strength he could muster.

As he flew up, the snake uncoiled himself, growing longer and longer until at last his head and his tail curled back towards the earth, his spine curving high up above as he scraped the blue ice off the sky.

The snake's body kept changing colour, from red to yellow and green and purple. The ice in the sky melted, and once again the welcome raindrops came showering down to the earth.

Everything came to life again; the water filled the dried up riverbeds, the animals returned to their native grounds, and the roses blossomed as usual. And what about the Indians?

The Indians lifted up their faces in joy, allowing the rain to stream down them, and they danced in honour of the snake, which ever since then has always curved his elastic body like a coloured ribbon above the earth whenever there is rain on a sunny day.

The Lost
Children

The buffalo herds wandered far and wide; nothing could stop them. But they avoided a solitary teepee at the riverside as if the spot where it stood were haunted.

Seven boys lived in that tent, poor as prairie mice. Their father rarely brought anything home from the hunt, and thus they often had to make do with singing and dancing instead of food.

Nor did they have anything to wear; whereas the boys from the nearby village put on new calf-skin clothes every spring, the seven brothers did their best to hide from sight, since they went naked and were afraid of ridicule.

They only ventured out of their teepee at night, when they played games in the hope of forgetting their empty stomachs. They would steal quietly out of their tent, making their way through the sleeping prairie to a certain well-sheltered place where the ground had been stamped bare and hard. And invariably before they began to play, they made a fire to drive away the cold.

Having gone without anything to eat all day, they tried to make up for it at night by holding a great feast. This, of course, was only a make-believe feast, without any food. As they crouched there over the flames, their imaginations conjured up tempting pictures of succulent roast bison. And then they would dance round the fire until the dawn's approach sent them off to bed.

Thus, night after night went by, and the seven brothers remained poor and hungry, for the Great Spirit had plenty of other things to worry about, with many Indians on the war path, and it never occurred to him for a moment that any of his children might be suffering.

By the end of the Yellow Calf Month, the seven boys were so emaciated and weak that they no longer even felt like playing and dancing.

'Come on, get up,' the eldest brother urged the other six. 'Let's light a council fire — it is sure to give us some saving idea.'

I don't know how many fires were burning in the Indian country that night, but I know well enough that one of them burned at the edge of the prairie and had seven boys sitting round it. For a long time they just sat still, saying nothing; then the youngest spoke up in a grave tone of voice:

'The world is a bad place, perhaps we had better leave it. Let us change into . . . well, into clay, for example. Then we shall be at peace and shall lack nothing.'

'No, the clay is dead. Let us rather change into a rock,' suggested the second brother.

'No, rocks are apt to crack,' disagreed the third. 'We'd better become huge trees.'

But the fourth brother had a different idea:

'The lightning might kill us. Let us become water, then we shall be safe and no one will be able to harm us.'

'What about the Sun?' asked the fifth brother. 'It will dry up any pool or river if it feels like it. Let us turn into night — night has always given us protection.'

They thought this a good idea and were about to agree, when the sixth brother stopped them by saying:

'No, not even the night is all-powerful. It is invariably followed by day, and what happens to it then? I think it would be better if we became the day and not the night.'

They were silent for a while, and then the eldest brother said:

'As you know, the day too does not last for ever. Only the blue sky is eternal. We cannot become the blue sky, for one blue sky is enough for the Indians. But there are beautiful things up there in the sky called the stars. I'm sure they'll gladly accept us into their midst.'

The boys rejoiced to hear these wise words. Yes, that was the answer; they would turn into stars!

They threw the remaining logs on the fire, which grew bigger and brighter, lighting up the entire clearing.

This was what the brothers were waiting for. They got to their feet, joined hands, and slowly, very slowly, started to dance.

Their tiredness seemed to evaporate with each step they took; their legs flashed faster and faster, but still they did not stop. Now they were hardly touching the ground with their feet any more, and, still holding hands, they rose in a circle upwards. Far below the fire slowly went out, but they rose higher and higher, up to Wakinu's White Trail.

Immense are the starry plains above the Indian country.

Now, when the night sky had encompassed them with its wonders, the seven brothers stopped dancing at last and looked round in amazement. They saw seven fairy-tale wigwams that seemed to be waiting for them and they ran forward, one boy to each tent.

Inside, a surprise lay in store for them all. On the walls of the wigwams, on the floors, and everywhere the eye could see, there were countless lovely objects, so that the seven boys stood looking on in breathless wonder at all the magnificent riches displayed there for their benefit. There were brand new, beautifully ornamented clothes, glittering chieftains' head-dresses, delicately fashioned moccasins, and an abundance of choice foods.

Each boy quickly donned the new clothes and ran out of his wigwam to show his brothers how lucky he had been.

Now they had yet another surprise — their clothes were all exactly alike, and they gleamed with a dazzling golden glow. They gazed at one another in great astonishment, wondering what had happened to them. It was the eldest brother who found the reply to their unvoiced question:

'The Great Spirit has fulfilled our wish,' he told them. 'He has called us to him and we've become stars.'

And it was really so. Ever since then, when autumn comes and the young buffaloes turn brown, all the children in the Indian country look up at the sky and count the lost brothers in the Pleiades cluster of stars. They but rarely succeed, however, for the eldest brother's wigwam stands higher than the rest and its glow is lost in the great measureless distance.

The White
Water-lily

In the days before the war drums sounded in the country of the Indians, a beautiful village stood at the edge of the prairie. The men went out to hunt every morning and returned every evening with rich booty, the women prepared their food and sewed clothing, and the children played from sunrise to sunset. Altogether they were all very happy and contented, happier than any other people in the world.

The Sun shone long into the afternoon, smiling down on the red men; the rain fell only when it was needed to replenish the wells and rivers and lakes with fresh water and to refresh the trees and flowers.

And now listen to what happened. The stars which every night flickered above the camp soon got to know about the Indians and, their lamps being so tiny that their light

never reached the earth, they begged their chieftain to let them go and visit the village.

The Moon was the chieftain of the night sky, and he did not like to have his people wandering about and going to bed late in the morning, like the Morning Star. Whenever they did so, he had disagreements with the Sun. But that night he was in an exceptionally good mood, and so he granted the stars their request. They quickly got ready for their journey, laughing and chattering, so that they hardly heard the wise counsel given them by the Moon.

'You may go wherever you please, only take care not to touch the ground. If you did that, you'd have to stay there, and the Sun would burn you to death the next day, for his arrows are fatal to us.'

The stars journeyed long and far. It was lucky for them that the Moon was full that night, as otherwise they would surely have lost their way. At long last they reached the Indian village and, hovering above it, examined it from all sides. The Indians were asleep, only one little boy who lived on the very fringe of the camp was still awake. Hearing a strange whispering noise above his head, he listened carefully, then he looked out through the opening at the top of his wigwam — and his heart almost stopped beating at the sight that met his eyes. So many stars so very, very near! He climbed right up to the top of the tent and moved the pole to get a better view. The pole caught against something and crash! the smallest and most inquisitive of the stars came hurtling down. It had just been passing low over the wigwam and now dropped to the floor, where it changed at once into a beautiful, weeping girl.

'Now look what you've done!' she reproached the boy. 'I can't return with my sisters, and as soon as dawn comes, the Sun's arrows will find me and I shall die.'

The boy stared at her in astonishment. The other stars had in the meantime realised what had happened and they fled back home in panic, knowing they could do nothing to help their unfortunate sister.

The tears streamed down the girl's lovely face, and the boy was overcome with pity.

'I'll help you,' he said. 'When the Sun is out during the day, I'll close my wigwam and he'll not be able to see you. But what shall we do after that?'

'If only I survive the day, I'll change into a flower in the evening and I'll go and live on top of a high cliff from which I will watch you and your people, for I like your Indian ways.'

They did exactly as they had agreed to do. The boy stayed at home that day, taking care that not even the slightest and most curious ray penetrated the wigwam. And as soon as the day was gone, the girl slipped away through the smoke opening and hurried to a high cliff, on top of which a beautiful white rose grew the very next morning.

All the Indians admired the flower from a distance, but only the boy knew that it was actually the little star he had sheltered in his wigwam from the deadly rays of the Sun.

Before long the girl began to feel very lonely up there on her hilltop. Though she could gaze far out into the country and could watch life in the camp, no one ever climbed the sheer cliff to chat with her. Only the birds nesting thereabouts would sometimes fly up to her and keep her company.

One day a small wren came to talk to her.

'I am so lonely here,' the white rose complained. 'I miss human company. If only I could live down there on the prairie.'

'If that's what you want, I can easily help you,' the kind little bird replied. 'Just bend your head a little so that I can take you in my beak.'

The rose obediently bent her head, the wren picked her up in his beak and flew away with her to the prairie.

There life was far gayer. The Indians as well as all kinds of animals came to tell the white rose the news. But then one morning a deep rumble could be heard in the distance. 'Hurry, hurry!' everyone cried. 'We must hide, the buffaloes are coming!' And they all ran and hid as best as they could. A great cloud of dust soon appeared on the horizon, growing larger and larger all the time. The white rose was badly frightened and she hid her head under her leaves that had broadened out in horror. Like a hurricane the herds went past, their thousands of hooves making a noise like thunder.

When at last all was quiet again, the white rose peeped fearfully out from her sheltering leaves. The prairie had been laid waste, there was no sign of life anywhere.

'I mustn't stay here and put myself in such terrible danger,' the star said to herself. 'I'll be better off on the lake.'

Detaching herself from the ground she soon saw beneath her the glittering surface of a lake. Like an Indian canoe she glided gently into the water.

When, early the next morning, the Indians sailed out on to the lake they found to their surprise that there were beautiful white flowers on its surface.

'The night stars have put out blossoms,' said the little children, but the wise men shook their heads and said: 'It is the white star, come to live with us.' They were right.

Since that day, then, the star has lived on the lake in the shape of a white water-lily, and the Indians call her Wahbegwanee, or White Blossom.

Sickness
and Medicine

Animals and people lived in peace with one another, not getting in each other's way until the time when some greedy Indians began to kill wild beasts only to sell their flesh and their fur.

The numbers of beavers and otters, stags and bison were quickly becoming smaller and smaller, and so one day the white bear called all the animals together for a conference.

They could not agree on the best way to avenge themselves on people. The bears advocated making war on them, and they produced some bows and arrows, only to find that their long claws made it impossible for them to shoot properly. The birds suggested carrying away the wicked hunters' wigwams, while the beaver thought it would be enough to gnaw holes in the bottoms of their canoes.

The flies gave the matter due consideration, buzzing excitedly inside a nearby hollow tree-stump; and when no one else could put forward any new ideas, the oldest and wisest among them stood up and, leaning on his club, told the assembled animals:

'We shall ask the spirits to send sickness down upon the Indians who are harming us. We, the flies, undertake to spread the disease.'

They all agreed to this, and the white bear declared the meeting over. The animals dispersed to their homes, wondering what would happen next.

And true enough, before long, sickness came to the Indian villages. But it did not choose its victims; it attacked everyone who happened to cross its path. No one went out hunting any more, and the Indians lay ill in their wigwams and starved, whether they were good or whether they were wicked.

The animals grew sad at this, for they had not meant the sickness to strike all of the Indians.

Thus they fell to thinking what should be done about it, and they asked one another for advice.

This, however, came from quite an unexpected quarter — from the herbs.

'We possess healing powers!' called out the flowers in forest and meadow. 'We'll soon heal the sick!'

The Indians ran out of their wigwams to collect wild thyme, centaury, strawberry leaves, the healing root of the fern, and every other sort of herb, hoping to be cured. And whenever they were undecided which medicine to use for which sickness, the good little spirits concealed in the flowers whispered and told them.

Thus it was that medicine was discovered; the red men had found that even the smallest things in nature could be of use to them.

The Dandelion

The children in the north would frequently ask why it was that Shawondasee, the South Wind, did not stay longer and why it did not chase the North Wind, Kabibonocca, back to its native haunts, to the Land of Ice in the far North. How nice it would have been to enjoy the summer all year long! But their elders explained:

'Shawondasee is fat and lazy; all he ever does is to lie at his ease and smoke. In this way he may manage to drive away his own sorrow, but never Kabibonocca.'

'And why is the South Wind sad?' the children wanted to know.

'Why is he sad?' one of the old men replied. 'I'll tell you. It happened like this:

'You all know that Shawondasee brings the summer. Once—he was still young in those days—he looked northwards over the prairie in our direction. The air was full of a summer fragrance and birdsong, and the sky was clear and blue—a wonderful day.

'Suddenly he caught sight of a beautiful girl a long way away. There she stood, all alone in the midst of flowers, slender as a stem herself; her hair had such a lustre that it dazzled his eyes to look at it.

'Shawondasee liked the look of her very much, but don't think for a moment that he troubled to go after her. He was a terribly lazy fellow even in those days long ago. All he did was to stand gazing at her until his eyes almost popped out of their sockets. And whenever he woke from his sleep, he would turn his head towards that meadow, to enjoy the beautiful sight. In the end he fell in love with the charming creature. Many were the times he felt tempted to set out in search of his beloved, who was always in front of his eyes like some lovely daydream, but his laziness invariably got the better of him and he fell asleep again. He was to pay dearly for his sluggishness.

'One morning he again looked to the north, and what did he see — the golden hair he had loved so much had turned silver, as if covered with hoarfrost!

'Of course he thought at once of Kabibonocca. And true enough, the North Wind had lured the girl away from him with his midnight tales, and he had bound her with frosty bonds and filled her hair with hoarfrost.

'Shawondasee wailed and lamented, bitterly regretting his laziness. He sighed and sighed, until his warm breath spread far and wide. Then a snowstorm broke over the prairie, and something that was white as snow fluttered in the air. As for the girl, she disappeared for ever.'

'How so? How could she disappear?' the children wanted to know.

'Listen, and I'll tell you,' the old man said, smiling. 'You see, it was no girl standing in that meadow. It was a yellow dandelion. And since Shawondasee is not only lazy but also unobservant, he failed to notice this and thought it was a girl. Then the dandelion lost its golden flower, and that was the silver hair. The South Wind had suspected Kabibonocca, and he sighed so much that he blew the dandelion's fluff all over the prairie. After that it was, of course, all in vain to look for the beautiful girl. So it was really all his own fault, but how can you expect anyone as lazy as Shawondasee to bother his head with thought and get to the bottom of things. And only the Indians know that when sadness spreads over the countryside at summer's end, Shawondasee is again sighing in sorrow, longing for his beloved, who is nothing but a figment of his imagination.'

The Old
Woman's Hair

Since time immemorial maize has served the Indians in place of wheat, for they did not know this kind of cereal and used maize flour to bake their bread and sweetmeats. There is a nice Indian legend about the way maize came into the world.

An old woman and her grandson once travelled through the Indian country. No one knew where they had come from nor where they were going, and no one asked the old woman to share their fire, although she asked and begged them to do so. That was a time when almost all the Indian tribes had taken up their tomahawks and warred with each other, so that every newcomer was suspected of being an enemy spy.

'Never mind,' the old woman said to her grandson. 'I'm sure we'll find some good people who will take care of us.'

And they continued on their way, over mountain and prairie, until they one day reached the camp of the Alligator tribe. These were very poor but good-hearted Indians, and they invited the old woman and her boy to their fire and shared the little they had to eat with their guests. Then the chieftain, Alligator Tooth, spoke to the pilgrims, saying:

'You can stay here with us, if you feel like it, but you should know that we often suffer from hunger. Our hunting-grounds are not rich in game, and moreover we have to sacrifice the best prey to the alligators if we do not wish to lose their favour.'

'We shall gladly share your fortune, whatever it may be,' replied the old woman. 'In return I'll look after all the children, so that I should not be entirely useless.'

And so, as soon as the next day dawned, all the hunters left the camp, followed shortly afterwards by all the women; only the youngest children were left behind.

True, the children were used to being by themselves all day long, and they played together quite happily. What they could not do, though, was to get their own food, and so they always had to go without until evening, when their parents might bring them something to eat.

Things were different now, with the children flocking round the old woman like chicks round an old hen, listening to her stories. She told them why it was that the earth was covered not only with the soft, low grass but also with tall trees. One day the mighty Manitou wished to stroke the blossoms which fluttered in the light breeze on the slender stems of flowers. But however much he leaned out of his heavens, he found he could not touch them. They were too far out of his reach. He therefore expressed the desire for the stems to grow until their blossoms touched the palms of his hands. Ever since then, slender pines and firs and maple-trees have been growing out of the earth, their magnificent crowns touching the skies. All Manitou has to do now is to put out his hand and he can stroke them to his heart's content, while their crowns gently wave to and fro, murmuring softly.

The old woman was not merely a fine story-teller — she also knew exactly when the small fry were getting hungry, at which times she would disappear from sight, to return a little later with a huge cauldron from which there rose a strange, appetising smell.

'This is maize gruel,' she explained. 'As long as you behave yourselves and do as you're told, you will get some every day.'

The months thus went by, until the last month — that of the Long Night — had come and gone. The old woman still kept making her tasty maize gruel for the children, but lately she seemed to be getting more and more frail, seeming to evaporate slowly like steam over the pot.

One morning she could no longer get up from her bed. She therefore called her grandson and told him:

'My dear, I know I shall soon leave the world of men, for the maize grains I sowed outside the camp have taken root and will sprout in the spring. I have done my part — now it is up to you and the rest of the children to look after them, to water and hoe them. Otherwise they will not yield a harvest . . .'

These were the last words the old woman ever spoke. Every day at noon she gave her grandson a cauldron of maize gruel, but the day when the first ear of maize ripened behind her wigwam she vanished, and no one ever saw her again, even though they all looked for her everywhere.

'We shall never see her again,' Alligator Tooth told them. 'Yet she will always remain with us. Look,' and he pointed to the maize growing all round their camp. 'She has changed herself into these plants which she brought us so that we should never go hungry again.'

Thus it was that the kind old woman repaid the tribe for their hospitality. And since then the Indians tend their maize fields carefully, and when white hairs sprout from the green ears of corn they see in them the white hair of the old woman they will never forget.

The Gift
of the Totems

Far beyond the four mountains and the four rivers, on the shores of a limitless ocean, there used to stand the Totem Village, called so on account of the tall, slender totem-posts standing behind each wigwam to give protection to the Indians as they sailed out to sea to hunt whales.

The fishermen believed that these carved and painted poles helped to ward off evil. They held them in high esteem, and whenever they came back from a successful trip they always held a *potlach*, or in other words a big feast, in their honour.

One night, just before one such *potlach*, a raven fell asleep in a tree near the totem grove. He must have had bad dreams or felt cold, for in the middle of the night he suddenly awoke; and as he listened there in the dark, trying to discover what it was that had disturbed his sleep, he heard soft, strange voices, as if the branches, buffeted by the wind, were conversing together.

The raven craned his neck a little, and the voices became more distinct. He had not been mistaken: the wooden totems were talking!

'What is thy opinion, O Highest of Totems?'

'The Spirit of the Great Cod-Fish tells me that the Indians are to receive a gift, and that this gift is to be a metal. A yellow, glittering metal like gold. Am I right, O Eldest of Totems?'

'The Spirit of the Wise Herring has told me in confidence that it must not be a metal as hard as gold, for that would harden the hearts of the red men. Dost thou agree, O Wisest of Totems?'

'Aye, for the Spirit of Mother Whale has informed me that out of this metal the Indians are to fashion the heads of their arrows, spears and lances.'

But though he listened as carefully as he could, the raven heard no more of the whispered conversation conducted by the totems.

'Anyway, I've heard enough,' he thought, making up his mind to watch very attentively at tomorrow's *potlach*, in order to gain some advantage for himself out of the gift the totems had mentioned. After all, he could not allow those stupid Indians to get everything while he went away empty-handed. . . .

The great *potlach* started even before the Sun had reached the middle of the sky. Ever since that morning, Indians from near and far had been arriving in their long boats with pointed prows, bringing precious gifts, such as coloured blankets, choice foods and beverages, and various weapons.

When all the guests had paid their respects to the totems in the grove and sat down in a circle, something quite unexpected and unforeseen happened: the air was suddenly agitated as if by the beating of thousands of birds' wings. The ocean rose up, and far in the distance, above the crests of the high-flung waves, a strange glittering object could be glimpsed, flying nearer and nearer.

And then, to the astonishment of the assembled Indians, the Highest of Totems addressed them in a human voice:

'The good spirits bring you a valuable gift. It is copper, from which you can make heads for your arrows, spears and lances. It will serve you far better than the flint you have been using hitherto.'

The Highest of Totems had not even finished speaking when, out of the blue, the raven appeared above the heads of the listening Indians and made straight for the brightly gleaming object in the sky, intending to carry it away with him. They looked up, dazzled by the glow and shocked by the raven's impudence. But the good spirits were vigilant and did not allow the bird to make off with their gift.

Now it seemed that all would be well, for the raven seemed to have realised the futility of his efforts and to be flying away. But then, taking everyone unawares, he returned in a flash, seized the glowing ball of copper from the surprised spirits, and was about to escape with it in his claws.

The copper proved too heavy for him, however. He managed to hold on to it for just a moment longer, but then had to let it drop into the sea, which buried the precious object in its depths.

'What's to be done now?' whispered the Indians, turning to the totems in the hope that they would give them some good advice. But the sacred poles stood there silent and motionless.

'Perhaps a clever and skilful fisherman can be found to salvage the precious gift with his harpoon,' said the chieftain, interrupting the profound silence that had settled over the assembly. 'If he succeeds, I shall give him my only daughter to be his wife.'

Hearing her father's words, the girl trembled and tears started to her eyes, for she had long ago pledged her troth to a brave hunter from their village; he had been gone for many days now, sailing distant seas to bring her a wedding present, and she had remained faithful to him all that time.

Yet, she could not oppose her father's decision. The others agreed with it, and some were indeed already casting off in their boats.

Lake Blossom—that was the name of the chieftain's beautiful young daughter—walked sadly to the totem grove, where she knelt in front of the Wisest of Totems.

'Oh, what am I to do? Please help me, O Wisest!' she pleaded.

Seeing that her heart was bursting with sorrow, the totem spoke to her in such low tones that only she was able to hear him:

'Put on a man's clothing. Then go along the seashore as far as the mouth of the Salmon Lake. There thou shalt find a canoe and inside it a harpoon. Put out to sea and take no notice of the waves which will play with the boat so boisterously that thou shalt learn the meaning of fear. The canoe will take thee to the spot where the ball of copper is to be found on the ocean bed. When it stops, pick up the harpoon and plunge it in so that it will pierce the copper. Then, having withdrawn the gift, sail back to the mouth of Salmon Lake. Shouldst thou not do exactly as I tell thee, know the waves will destroy thy boat and thou wilt perish in the sea. Now go and delay not. Howgh!'

Not for a moment did the girl hesitate. Putting on the clothes of one of her brothers, she smeared her face with coloured clay so that no one should be able to recognise her and hurried to the mouth of Salmon Lake. There she found a boat and a harpoon, and set out bravely to sea.

She soon found that the ocean was very wild, with treacherous whirlpools sucking at the canoe and huge waves all but swamping it; yet still the boat travelled on towards its important goal.

As she went, the chieftain's daughter could see the overturned boats of those who had made the attempt before her. None of them had got very far, paying with their lives for their courage and their desire to marry Lake Blossom; in their last minutes they had come to realise that the ocean would never voluntarily yield what it had once taken for its own.

The canoe stopped. Raising the harpoon, the girl looked down into the turbulent waters. Her hand trembled, but the thought of her beloved transformed her despair into strength. With all her might she plunged the harpoon into the waters, and as soon as she felt it strike home, began to pull it out again.

The raging waves tossed the canoe about at their will; and when at last she had extracted the copper ball from the depths, the ocean lashed at her boat in real fury. It roared and bucked like a wild mustang, and the girl was certain she would be swallowed up by it at any moment. Yet she always emerged out of the tumbling waves, and before long had landed on the shore of Salmon Lake.

Shouts of joy greeted her on the shore, where all the people from her village had in the meantime assembled. The chieftain himself bent down to take the copper ball from the bottom of her canoe; but as he lifted it to show it to the crowd, the raven again swooped down on it, croaking prodigiously. Wrenching it out of the astonished chieftain's hands he flew with it to the top of the tallest pine, as if the evil spirits themselves had endowed him with strength.

'Now I've got your gift, and you needn't expect me to return it to you!' the raven shouted triumphantly. 'I shan't return it!' he croaked every time an arrow whistled through the air, as the desperate Indians tried to regain their treasure

The girl, too, attempted to shoot the thieving raven. They all knew who she was by now, since her head-dress had slipped and her bluish-black hair had come tumbling down her back. But not even her arrows managed to reach the top of the pine.

At that moment quick footfalls were heard coming from Salmon Lake. A young man came running, lightly as a deer. As soon as he was near enough to be recognised, the girl ran forward to meet him and fell into his arms.

'At last you've come, my dearest!' she cried. And as she embraced him, she told him what had happened. Wave Flier, as the young man was nicknamed because of the great skill with which he guided his canoe, took an arrow from his quiver, put it to his bow and, waiting for the insolent raven to show his head, sent it flying in the bird's direction.

In the tense silence all that could be heard was a fierce cry emitted by the raven and

the whistling noise made by the arrow. Then came a crackling sound from the top of the tree as the raven dug his claws into the bark in his death throes — and the fiery ball of copper dropped down to earth.

The copper ball hit the ground and broke into a thousand small pieces. The raven was right, thought the Indians — he stole our gift from us and now he has destroyed it and made it useless.

'That is not so,' said a voice from the spot where stood the Wisest of Totems. 'It is from these very splinters that you will be able to make the sharpest arrow-heads and blades.'

And while the Indians were busy picking up the pieces of copper, the girl turned to the lucky marksman. Stretching out her hand to him, she asked:

'What gift have you brought me, dearest?'

'A small gift indeed,' the young man replied. 'I did catch a large whale, probably the largest whale in the world, but in Whale Bay I made a present of it to some Indians who were dying of hunger. This is all I kept — it is called ambergris.' And he handed the girl a wooden casket full of an ointment that gave off a heady scent.

Lake Blossom put the ointment on her hands and face and then she accompanied her betrothed to the totem grove. Behind the happy couple walked a crowd of Indians, led by their chieftain. He could not take his eyes off the two young people in front of him. And those nearest to him could hear him whisper:

'You have chosen wisely and well, my daughter. Wave Flier will be a good and faithful husband to you as long as you live.'

The Indians
and Death

In those days long ago neither the Indians nor the animals were subject to Death. They all lived for ever, and there was yet enough room for everyone. Only the coyote, discontented grumbler that he was, went about grousing: 'Why do we have to be squashed here like this? If only the old were to die, we'd be far better off.' And he ran all over the prairie,

shouting so loudly that he could be heard in both forest and desert. But no one paid any heed to his talk, for it was well-known that the coyote was a scoundrel who always tried to make trouble for everything and everybody.

This time, however, it soon became apparent that he would not so easily give up the idea that had lodged firmly in his crooked, dishevelled head. And when the snow remained lying on the ground especially long that year and famine threatened, he again started to shout:

'There, you see? I told you! There are too many of us, and that's why we are hungry. If only the old were to die, there would be plenty to eat for all of us.'

In the end the Great Shaman heard of the coyote's suggestions. The wise old man became very angry and wanted to punish the evil-minded ruffian, but then he thought better

of it and decided to call a meeting, which he hoped would prove to the coyote how repugnant his suggestion really was to one and all. Perhaps, thought the Great Shaman, the coyote may yet mend his ways.

And thus the Indians and the animals assembled at the foot of the Sacred Rock, with the Great Shaman sitting on a tree-stump on top of the cliff; his head-dress touched the sky when he raised his head to address them in the following words:

'My children! I could no longer bear to listen to the yelping of your brother coyote, who keeps proposing that we bring Death into the world. That is why I have now called you together. Tell the coyote what you think of his idea, so that he may be taught a lesson.'

The animals conferred together quietly, while the coyote sat alone, scratching behind his ears with his paw and getting up every now and again to trot from one to the other, pricking up his ears to hear what they were saying.

All of a sudden he called out:

'O Great Shaman, I never intended to harm anyone! But there isn't enough food to go round, and we can't all survive.' His cunning eyes were narrowed into mere slits. 'It was never my intention that those who die should not return to this world.'

'What is it you suggest, then?' asked the squirrel.

'I would tell you, only . . . I don't know, nobody trusts me, that's the trouble.'

'Go on, tell us!' the Indians urged him, and the Great Shaman leaned forward in order to hear him better.

'Very well, then,' said the coyote. 'I suggest we make a hole in heaven, and all the dead can move there for a time. Then, when there is again enough food for all, we'll simply call them back.'

'But there isn't a tree so high,' murmured the bear.

'I have thought it all out,' replied the coyote smugly. 'An Indian arrow will reach the sky. Then a second arrow can be shot to join up with the first, then a third and a fourth, until they link heaven and earth. Anyone can climb up then, and it will be even easier to get down again.'

The coyote's proposal seemed sensible enough. A little too pat, the Great Shaman said to himself; but think as he might, he could find no objection. Even the most sceptical among them approved of the idea. The coyote was smiling benevolently. If only they knew!

In the meantime the Indians had run off to fetch their bows and arrows, bringing as many as they could carry. Then the best marksmen prepared to shoot.

Whizz! the first arrow whistled over their heads and pierced a low cloud. It was immediately followed by another, which split the first arrow all the way up to its feather ornament and stuck fast.

The animals looked on in admiration as the Indians displayed their marksmanship. Not a single arrow went astray. The coyote ran about under the bowmen's legs, getting in the way and giving advice as if it had been he who had taught them to shoot.

Now the long line of arrows reached down as far as the Sacred Rock. The Great Shaman rose from his tree-stump, and he pulled at the arrows to test their strength. They held firm, strong enough to take even a bear's weight.

By this time dusk had set in, and the Great Shaman motioned with his hand for the crowd to disperse and go home.

'Go to sleep now, but as from this day, Death will be here with us; it is you who have decided so. I shall now open a door in the Sacred Rock for Death to come through, and those whom it chooses will climb up to heaven to stay there for a certain time....'

Night settled over the countryside — the first night in which Death walked the Indian country, the first night during which an old badger died in his den, a lonely hunter in his cabin, and an eagle in his eyrie high up among the rocks.

The dead walked in the dark to the Sacred Rock, and before dawn the last of them had vanished inside the hole in the star-filled sky.

Time passed. Soon the weeping of the bereaved could be heard everywhere, and many went to the Great Shaman for advice. But even he was powerless to help for the time being.

'We must wait for the stars to sink a little lower,' he told all comers. 'As they are now, they cannot hear us calling.'

Night after night, therefore, people as well as animals fixed their eyes on the sky, waiting for the return of those who had left them.

Only the coyote was nowhere to be seen. He had taken to his lair, and those who passed by it heard strange grating noises coming from inside. They wondered what the old rascal might be doing, but mostly they were convinced that he was afraid to come out in case they wanted to punish him for his little prank that had caused all the trouble.

However, a new and even more dastardly plan had taken shape in that crooked skull of his. The coyote had brought sharp-edged stones to his lair and now spent long days sharpening his teeth on them, making his fangs sharper than the Indian tomahawk. It was this that produced those strange sounds that could be heard coming from his lair.

When at last he all but cut his own tongue on his teeth, the coyote decided he had done all he could to prepare himself for the task in hand, and he went out quietly into the night.

It was the last hour before dawn, and everything was absolutely still. The coyote crept stealthily up to the Sacred Rock, putting his paws down cautiously so as not to give himself away by as much as a disturbed blade of grass.

He stopped at the foot of the cliff and listened. There was complete silence everywhere, only the night wind could be heard whistling in the rock crevices. There was thus nothing to prevent him from carrying out his evil intent. Standing up on his hind legs, he caught hold of the last arrow with his teeth and began to gnaw at it. The soft wood soon gave way, but the remaining arrows were still firmly attached to the sky. This infuriated the coyote — in his rage he shook the line of arrows furiously, hoping to pry the first one loose from the cloud above.

He succeeded only too well; with a resounding crash, the arrows came tumbling down about his ears. Some landed on his back with a thump, and the coyote squealed with pain: 'Wowww! Wowww!'

Bruised and battered, he crept back to his lair. Pandemonium broke out. The noise had awakened the bear and he, discovering what had happened, quickly roused the others, as well as the Great Shaman.

But there was nothing to be done — the dead could now never return to the land of the living again.

The Great Shaman was very angry. Without a moment's hesitation he pronounced judgment over the culprit:

'You must leave our midst as punishment. We were long patient with you, hoping that you might mend your ways, but all to no avail. Now go out into the prairie, where you will henceforth live alone, so that you should not do any more mischief.'

The coyote heard the verdict and, seeing that there was no other way, trotted off humbly, his tail between his legs.

He wandered a whole day long and perhaps even longer, finally settling down in a lonely spot where there was no other living creature for miles around — so afraid was he of the wise magician.

Now at last he began to regret his evil ways, and ever since then he has been wailing and begging to be allowed to return. But though his pleas are often to be heard, no one takes pity on him and calls him back, just as Death, whom he so carelessly brought into the world, will never go back to its abode in the Sacred Rock.

The Eternal Song

Night had come. The Indian country was lost in such darkness that no one as much as stuck his nose out of his teepee; only the solitary wind sighed in the distant hills.

And yet there were some people walking along the overgrown path that leads alongside the Serpent Creek. They went forward cautiously, making no sound. The Dakotas were on the warpath, and here a company of warriors was hurrying to surprise the enemy before the night was out.

The braves were silent, alternately walking and running, with look-outs in front and at the rear to guard against surprise attack.

The Serpent Creek left the plain and led them to a small grove.

'Let us rest here,' said their chieftain, speaking out loud for the first time. 'This is a desolate place — we can light a fire.'

In an instant the warriors brought some dry grass and kindling, and they soon got the fire going. Then they settled themselves comfortably around it, some repairing their torn moccasins, others examining their bows, arrows and tomahawks, and still others preparing their food.

The oldest among them meanwhile told of long-ago battles and of the strange adventures of famous heroes. They told how the mighty talisman had saved numerous lives; how a magic pouch had turned an enemy's arrow and sent it back to pierce the heart of the one who had discharged it; how beautiful girls came from the Land of Shadows to lead the bravest away to regions from which there was no return.

The fire listened to these many tales, sending its silent smoke up to the green branches; but then, just as a white-haired old Indian got up to say the solemn prayer, it suddenly roared and crackled, shooting out sparks all around the camp circle.

Just then something even stranger than this happened.

A song was heard, coming from the nearby trees.

The voice grew in volume, filling the grove with a sad melody, only to drop again and blend with the wailing of the wind in the branches.

'Put out the fire!' the chieftain ordered in a whisper; his bow held ready in his hands, he stepped forward into the dark.

As if obeying some secret command, the Moon now swam out from among the rolling

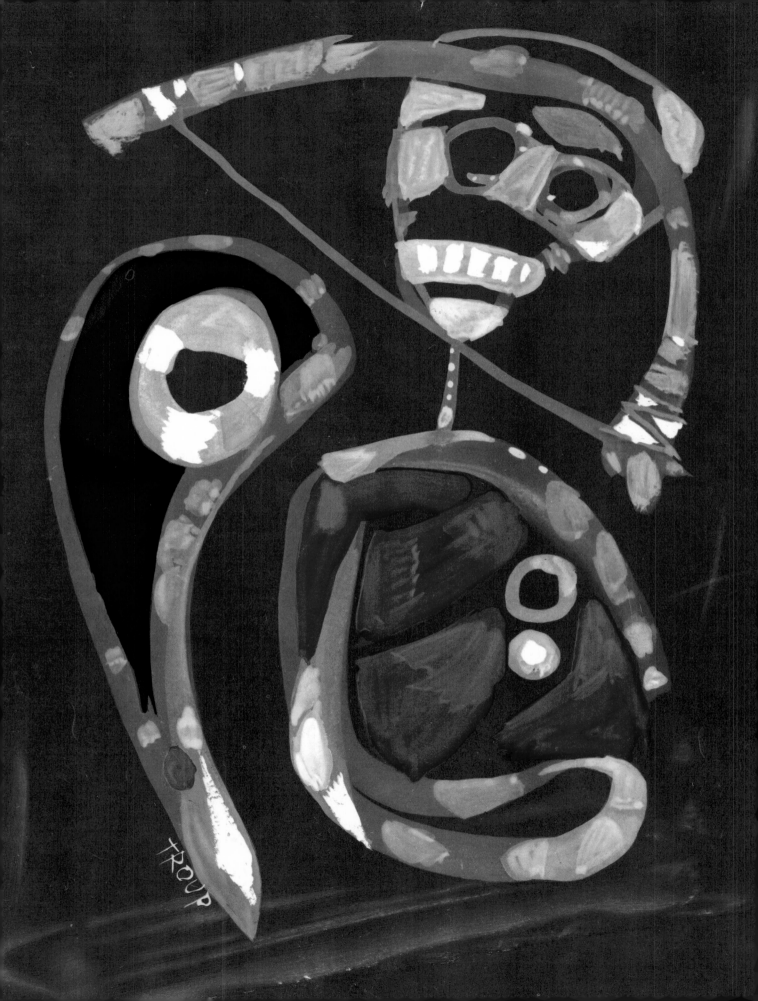

clouds, its pale glow illuminating the white tree-trunks. The warriors trod carefully in the soft, wet grass, watching the shadows of the crooked branches, swinging in the wind. The song went on. And now it was clear that it came from a huge spreading elm at the other end of the grove.

The warriors formed a circle and slowly walked forward, step by step, the circle narrowing all the time. The mysterious song rose to a shrill note and then ended as suddenly as it had begun. The warriors walked up to the old tree, their eyes travelling over the time-ravaged trunk until they came to rest in the tangled roots.

There, they could see a small pile of whitened bones belonging to some unknown warrior; next to the skull there lay a broken bow, and a little farther off were several scattered arrows.

'That which we have just heard and seen is a proof that this is the last resting-place of a warrior who sacrificed his life for others,' the chieftain broke the long silence at last.

'Not even Death can still the voice of such as he,' the chieftain continued, 'and his song goes on until it reaches the ears of the living and evokes the proper response. This has just happened, and now it is we who must carry the song and its message about the most sacred duty which urges us to sacrifice ourselves for others. It is up to us to keep this song in mind until the time when we ourselves shall journey to the Land of Shadows. Then our song, too, will become immortal and eternal. Howgh!'

The Duel Between the Great Spirit and God

'It is late, and you're tired,' said the calumet after a brief pause, and it sent up a puff of smoke. 'You ought to be turning in.'

'Oh no, not yet,' pleaded the boy. 'And there's something I'd like to ask you . . .'

'All right, go ahead and ask, but be quick about it — the tobacco is coming to an end, and my voice grows weak.'

'Tell me, who is this Great Spirit, and where does he live?'

'The Great Spirit is the most powerful of all the Indian spirits, and he resides in the High Wigwam in heaven. Though, to tell you the truth, he may be everywhere at one and the same time.'

'And has no one ever vanquished him?'

'No, no one ever has. True, the pale-faces did once, many many years ago, send their own God to drive the Great Spirit from the Indian country, but Manitou came out of the duel as the victorious one.'

'Oh, do tell me about it,' the boy demanded.

'Very well, I'll tell you the story as I have heard it told by the Hurons. But that will really be all for today. Now listen . . .

The Great Spirit was sitting on top of the Sacred Rock when suddenly God appeared there next to him.

'Gowa!' Manitou greeted him affably, but the newcomer did not deign to reply; all he did was to keep looking round with a gloomy look on his face.

'Why dost thou not speak to me?' the Great Spirit asked him.

'I'm mightier than thou, and I shall drive thee from this place!' was the reply.

'Oh, do thou but try!'

God said nothing, but kneeling down on the ground, produced a black book and began to whisper something the Great Spirit could not understand. When this had been going on for some time and still nothing happened, Manitou suggested:

'We shall never be able to match forces in this way. Dost thou see the rock I'm sitting on?' God nodded absent-mindedly.

'He who first manages to shift it, will remain in the Indian country,' the Great Spirit said. 'Go on and try.'

God opened his black book once more; he read and read, but he had already turned over the last page and still the rock did not move.

'Can't be done!' cried God in chagrin.

Then the Great Spirit got to his feet. Pulling up his leather sleeves he pushed hard against the rock. A great crash was heard — and the rock had moved a stag's leap further on.

'Didst thou see?' Manitou asked his adversary. But God had gone — he ran and ran, raising the dust behind him, and was never seen in the Indian country again.

Forest Lore
and Tales
about Animals

'I have been waiting for you,' puffed the calumet when the boy sat down by the blazing fire the following evening. Rain was pattering on the windows and the roof, but inside it was cosy and warm.

'The Indians have always lived out in the open and they understood the ways of nature,' the calumet said by way of introduction. 'Thus, for instance, a brook in the forest would tell them:

' "I sing when you drink from me and the gentle clouds or the stars look down on us from on high."

' "I am your brother and I protect you against beasts and the cold," the fire would announce in its crackling tones to the Indian hunter.

' "I am your sister; you can read from me as from the most truthful of books," whispered the grass.'

'And did the red men understand all this?' asked the boy a little doubtfully.

'Of course, and more. They also knew the habits of animals and the healing powers of plants. To put it in a nutshell, they were well up in forest lore, and tonight I'll tell you some of the stories I have learned from them about nature and animals. Now listen carefully . . .'

How the Indians Came to Own Horses

An orphan boy lived in one of the Indian villages on the banks of the Great River. His was the smallest mud hut, and since he was too young and weak to be able to carry arms, he had to beg good people for something to eat. But many a time he was driven away, the people saying, 'Why should we feed you? You're no good for anything — even a puppy can carry heavier burdens.'

In those days, you see, the Indians did not have horses — perhaps Tirawa, the Great Spirit, had forgotten to give them this animal — and so they either had to use dogs for carrying their loads or carry them themselves.

Only the chieftain never failed to give the boy something to eat, and he even made him a present of a pair of moccasins. 'Tirawa knows why this boy is alive, and maybe he will one day grow up to be a great hero,' the chieftain told his people, but not many really believed this. What kind of a hero could such a poor weakling become?

In the spring, as soon as the thunder of bison hooves could be heard in the distance and the first black manes appeared on the horizon, the Indians left their homes to follow the herds, which supplied them with meat and skins for the winter. That was the day the boy feared most, for then he would be abandoned by all, remaining alone in the camp, where it was difficult to procure anything to eat. In previous years it had often happened that on coming back the villagers found him so weak and famished that it was a wonder he did not die.

One early morning in the Month of Flowers the sentries spotted the familiar black manes down by the river. 'Bison, bison!' the cry went up. 'The bison are coming!' And before the sun's first rays penetrated the veil of mist, the village was quite empty.

The boy sat despondently in front of his mud hut, watching the dust which was slowly settling on the track as the last men and dogs disappeared from view, their voices and barking still audible a long time after they had vanished in the prairie.

He was left all alone. Glistening tears ran down his face and fell on to his moccasins. How he would have liked to have gone with the others!

The dust grew moist with his tears. Suddenly it seemed to him that he could hear a soft, urgent voice telling him:

'Go on and play. Show what your weak fingers can do!'

Who had spoken to him? And what was he to play with? His eyes rested on the small mound of dust under his feet which his tears had turned into sticky mud. It seemed just the thing to model with.

'I'm going to make myself a dog — then at least I shan't feel so lonely any more,' he said to himself, and began to mould the soft mud with his fingers. But what was this? Instead of the short legs possessed by dogs he turned out four long limbs with hooves. And the head was too long for a dog, with sharp, pointed ears, something like a mane on the neck, and at the rear end a tail quite unlike a dog's. What had he made? He had never seen an animal like it before.

'Let me try again, and I'll be more careful this time,' he told himself. But however much care he took, it was as if someone were guiding his hand, for he again moulded the same kind of animal as before.

He looked perplexed at the two figurines. There they stood on the ground in front of him, looking as if they were about to leap into the air at any moment. Suddenly he felt very tired. Stretching himself out on the dry ground he fell asleep at once; and this was the dream that came to him:

The great Tirawa himself came from his abode in the measureless distance. Now he could already make out his countenance and hear his wise words:

'It was I who made you play. At my bidding your fingers fashioned the horses, which you can now use to pull your loads or to carry you. But as they are far too small, you must

graze and water them for four days and four nights by the Great River, to make them grow and serve you well.'

Tirawa finished speaking, and his face dissolved in sleep like a ripple on the surface of the water.

The boy woke up, took both the figurines under his arm, and hurried down to the Great River. He knew well enough where the juiciest and most fragrant grass was to be found. He laid the figurines carefully on the ground, and in a trice the horses came alive, and they even neighed a little. The boy could not take his eyes off them. It was the miracle of miracles — they grew larger and stronger as he looked at them.

He let them eat their fill of grass and drink their fill of water and then, in the evening, led them back to the village. In that short space of time they had grown so much that they only just squeezed into his small hut, and the next night he had to put them up in the chieftain's large dwelling.

The boy rejoiced to see his horses grow so big and strong. On the morning of the third day he rode on their backs to and fro through the village. He felt an urge to go and find his friends and neighbours. He forgot all about the mighty Tirawa's counsel and, fording the Great River, rode with his two little horses in the footsteps of the bison herd.

Inexperienced as he was, the boy had never seen a horse before, and thus it seemed to him that they would not have grown any larger on the fourth day, anyway. But the great Tirawa was watching him. His countenance grew a little overcast, since he had meant to give the Indians a large horse such as that owned by the pale-faces, but then he realised that a smaller animal was after all nimbler and would suit the Indians better in hunting. And that is why the Indian horse is called a pony, meaning little horse.

In a little while the boy saw smoke coming from the hunters' encampment. The journey had not seemed at all long to him on horseback.

The chieftain and several astonished hunters came out to meet him. They could not take their eyes off the ponies. As for the boy, he was no longer a wretched, weak child but a sturdy youth who might easily become a chieftain in several years' time.

And he really did. Before long he excelled all the others at hunting, shooting and riding, so that when the old chieftain left them to join his ancestors, they picked the boy to take his place, and he ruled the red men wisely and for many years.

The Owl
and the Yellow Mouse

The owl dozed in her cave in the heat of noonday. She was unable to fall asleep and wondered what was happening outside now that she was supposed to be sleeping.

She was an extraordinarily vain bird, and she wanted everyone to be afraid of her. But unfortunately, during the daytime when most of the animals were abroad, she always slept in her cave, while at night, when she hooted hard in an attempt to outhoot the echo, everything was still and no one stirred.

'Ah, they've all hidden from me — they're afraid, that's what it is!' the owl chuckled. 'Oooo-hooo!' she hooted as loud as she knew how.

But still she was not satisfied.

'I think it would be just as well to go and ask someone what they think of me,' she muttered to herself that fine summer day. 'I needn't go far, come to think of it — there are dozens of yellow mice living under this rock; I'll go and ask *them.*'

She hopped about inside for a few moments longer (if the truth were told, she did not really feel like venturing out in the daytime) but then at last she flew out of her dark cave.

'An owl! An owl!' shrieked the mice as soon as they caught sight of her, and they scattered for home as fast as they could.

This was very much to the owl's liking. She settled down by the nearest mousehole and tried to peer inside.

'Hullo there, mouse! Don't be scared!' she called out. 'Are you there?'

'Yes, I am,' replied the little yellow mouse. She knew well enough that the owl could not harm her while she remained inside, but all the same she did not feel too comfortable.

'All I want is to ask you something,' the owl tried to ingratiate herself. 'You must tell me what it is they call me hereabouts.'

'So that's it!' said the mouse to herself. 'That's why the silly old hag is lurking outside my hole in the daytime.' But aloud she only said:

'They call you the Night Chieftain.'

This was like music to the ears of the vain owl.

'Say it again, but more slowly this time,' she ordered.

'Night . . . Chief . . . tain,' called out the mouse, shaking with fury. 'How conceited she is,' she said to herself angrily. 'The ugly monster!'

The owl was transported with joy.

'And now whisper it to me,' she said, putting her ear close to the mousehole.

This was too much for the little yellow mouse, and she cried:

'You're an old, miserable witch, that's what you are!' and she vanished deep inside her hole.

The owl at first only blinked her eyes, unable to understand; but then she was seized with fury.

'You wait till I catch you!' she threatened the yellow mouse. 'I'll teach you a lesson! And I shan't budge from here till you come out, either,' she added, pecking vengefully at the opening with her beak.

The mouse, of course, waited no longer, but slipped through the passageway to her friends, whom she at once told what had happened.

In the meantime the owl was still waiting outside the mousehole, stepping from one foot to the other. She was to pay dearly for her vanity and rage: she spent a day and a night outside the hole, then another, and a third, and I don't really know how many more, until in the end she perished of hunger and thirst — a victim of her own folly and vanity.

The Enchanted Stag

When winter draws to an end in the region of the maple-tree, the children leave their snug wigwams, wading through the melting snow and eagerly searching for the sweet sap yielded by the trees in spring.

These are joyous and exciting days, and little Kato and Wabi always looked forward to them very much. This particular spring, however, they were both unusually sad and quiet, and the other children, noticing this, asked them:

'What's the matter with you two? Why don't you play with us?'

Kato burst into tears instead of replying, while Wabi said:

'Our stepmother has driven us out. She says we're big enough to fend for ourselves and why should she have to bother with us. What are we to do now but leave the village?'

'But where would you go? The woods are full of wild beasts and evil spirits.'

'Oh, I'm not afraid,' Wabi replied. 'I have a fine bow and good arrows. Come, Kato,' he said, turning to his sister. 'It's high time we were on our way if we wish to put up our wigwam while it's still light.'

He gave her his hand and together they set out along the path leading out of the village into the deep forest.

They walked on and on. The path vanished in places, to reappear again a little farther off, and as they went they heard all the different, mysterious noises of the woodland, the shrill cries of birds, the rustle of the undergrowth, the cracking of tree-bark. It grew steadily darker, and every now and again it seemed to them that they could see wild, grinning faces in the murky twilight. Or again, like a fleeting shadow, a black bird would flit among the tree-trunks.

Badly frightened, Kato clung to her brother's hand, and he could tell that she was trembling all over.

'We'll soon be out of the wood,' he tried to reassure her.

'Ooo! Oooo!' came back the echo of his last word.

'Don't look about you,' he advised Kato, and the girl hung her head, while Wabi peered to the right and to the left. Yellow, green and purple faces hopped from tree to tree, from bush to bush, putting out long, emaciated arms towards them.

'Look — a trail!' the girl cried suddenly, pointing to the ground.

She was right. There were tracks under their feet which told Wabi that a huge stag must have passed by here not long before them.

'The tracks will lead us out of the forest,' he said pluckily.

As soon as they had set out along the stag's trail, the terrifying apparitions vanished. Then the trees grew sparser, and soon the two children found themselves in a large clearing. The grass was green here, and there was not the slightest trace of snow. The tracks continued, leading them to an old, spreading oak-tree in the middle of the clearing.

'I feel thirsty,' complained Wabi when they had stopped in the shadow of the enormous tree. No sooner were these words out of his mouth than the last footprint filled with clear, pure water.

The boy knelt down to drink.

'Don't, dear brother,' Kato warned him. 'This is no ordinary footprint.'

But Wabi ignored his sister's caution and drank eagerly and deeply.

He at once felt a strange languor possess his limbs; his head grew heavy, whereas his hands and feet itched with a desire to leap and dance.

'Oh, what is this? What's happened to you?' wailed Kato. 'You're growing a white fur, and there are antlers on your head!'

Wabi tried to rise from the ground, but his hands seemed clumsy all of a sudden. Instead of fingers he now had hooves, with which he in vain tried to catch hold of the tree. He could no longer speak, the only sound he produced being a trumpeting roar. He had turned into a white stag.

Kato wanted to help him, but to no avail: she spoke to him and even tried to remove his antlers. Finally, tired out after her long day's journey, she leaned her head against the stag's warm fur and fell asleep.

It was just midnight when Kato came awake with a start. She heard the breeze whispering in the leaves of the solitary tree. And she also heard a voice saying:

'So now I've got rid of them once and for all!'

It was the voice of her stepmother!

'No one will ever be able to help Wabi now, unless they were to fell this tree.'

'Ha, ha, ha,' another unpleasantly grating voice replied with a hoarse laugh. 'That will never happen!'

Kato looked up, but the thick foliage of the oak tree made it impossible to see anything.

Then, quite suddenly, the breeze as well as the voices died down. A chill moon wandered across the night sky, and the girl fell asleep again.

Next morning she recalled what she had heard. Without saying anything to the white stag, she made herself a small flint axe and with it tried to fell the tree. But no sooner had she struck at the thick trunk than her puny little tomahawk splintered into a hundred little pieces.

Disappointed, she sank on to the grass. The stag huddled up close to her.

'If only you knew, Wabi,' said Kato, stroking his head, 'I don't think I'll ever be strong enough to bring down that tree — and you can't help me.'

She wondered how she could fell the massive oak, but in the end there was nothing left for her to do but build herself a wigwam and wait. The stag went out to graze every day, coming back each evening.

One day at noon Kato heard shouts coming from the forest, and shortly afterwards the white stag came running, pursued by hunters. Arrows whistled through the air as they tried to shoot him. The stag stopped next to the oak tree, trembling all over. Kato intrepidly stepped in front of him to shield him with her body.

The Indian hunters lowered their bows and approached the strange couple. And as they came up closer, Kato recognised one of them as her father.

'Kato! What're you doing here?' he cried. lifting her up in his arms. 'And where's your brother Wabi?'

She pointed to the white stag and told the hunters everything that had happened.

The men listened attentively to her story. When it was over, they grasped their tomahawks and struck repeatedly at the oak tree, so that splinters flew to every side, yet not even they were able to fell it.

'Let's light a fire and burn down the oak,' suggested one of them.

They accordingly piled brushwood round the tree and set fire to it. Before long, tongues of flame were licking at the coarse bark. The fire bit into the oak, deeper and deeper all the time. Then they heard a great cracking and rending, and the huge oak toppled and fell majestically to the ground.

Kato was watching her brother and she saw how his antlers and white fur gradually disappeared as the tree came crashing down to earth. Wabi, the boy, again stood in front of her where the white stag had been only a few seconds before.

A cloud of black smoke billowed out of the fire, and they all saw a large black owl come flying out with it, screeching and winging its way into the forest.

'A witch! A wicked witch!' the hunters cried.

'Yes, that's right,' said Wabi softly. 'Our stepmother was a witch, and now, changed into an owl, she'll undergo her punishment by having to live with all the evil spirits in the forest.'

The Golden Cranes

Far, far away, a thousand sleeps distant from the Land of Many Rivers, there used to live a tribe of large golden birds called cranes. The wise Manitou had given them golden plumage and called their chieftain, Latakini, to him and spoken to him thus:

'Latakini, thou art the chieftain of the loveliest of all birds. I have given golden feathers to no other tribe but thine. For this, you must never leave the territory I have assigned you. That is my condition.'

'Why must we not fly away?' asked Latakini.

'Your feathers would lose their golden sheen,' replied the Great Spirit, and he soared up into the air and dissolved. Only the crowns of the pines still waved gently to and fro with the impact of his breath.

Latakini ruffled his golden plumage with his long beak; then he spread out his mighty wings and rose majestically into the air, on his way to announce to his people the decision of the great Manitou.

The summer was growing old, and the first flocks of Canadian geese, wild ducks and coots gathered in the Far North, in Latakini's native region, calling all the migratory birds together for their regular journey south.

Latakini felt more and more uneasy. For days on end he watched the huge flocks of birds vanishing over the horizon, night after night he listened to the beating of wings as more and more flights traversed the darkened skies. And when one morning he found that the cranes were the only ones left in the whole region he could no longer resist the temptation, and, soaring up, gave the signal for their long journey.

Manitou was very angry with the golden cranes for their disobedience. He knew that they were flying to the Land of Many Rivers, so he gave orders to all the water in that land to strip Latakini's tribe of their gold.

The cranes flew by day and by night, passing over unknown lands until at last they found themselves over the sunny prairie with its silver threads of rivers and glittering lakes. They had reached the Land of Many Rivers.

Latakini folded his wings, circled the lake, and then sailed slowly down to its surface, followed by the entire tribe. No sooner had he landed, however, than a storm seemed to break, with waves rising so high that they threatened to drown the birds. The turbulent waters plucked their golden feathers and carried them away, as they had been ordered by Manitou.

Latakini now called on his followers to fly off again, but it was too late. Instead of golden cranes there now flew under the southern sun a flock of white birds — and at that moment Latakini remembered the warning of the Great Spirit.

'Perhaps when we return north in the spring, Manitou will gild our feathers anew, and we shall then never disobey him again and shall stay there,' Latakini consoled himself.

He could hardly wait for spring to come, and as soon as he saw the first flocks returning home he urged his people to take wing as well.

Again they flew for many days and nights, not resting until they had reached their native region. They landed in the grass — and it was as if the snow had fallen once more, for the cranes remained white. And now Latakini knew that he would never again have golden feathers because he had gone against the wishes of the Great Spirit.

When Friends Fall Out

One day the mole received a very strange letter. It was a long blade of grass, full of different knots, each of which stood for a different word in the animal language of that time. Having unravelled the message with some difficulty he realised it contained an invitation for him to go to the Dry Island; and he was surprised to discover that it was signed by four great chieftains — the fox, the raven, the hare, and the bear.

'I should hurry,' the mole said to himself, 'for this is certain to be a matter of some importance.' And he went at once to prepare for the journey.

Having quickly tidied up his wigwam near an ancient maple tree, he brushed his velvet coat and started out on his trip. He was quite breathless by the time he reached the lake shore and, swimming across with great difficulty since he was so tired, he at last arrived on the Dry Island.

The four chieftains were there, waiting for him.

'Now we're all here, we might as well begin,' said the bear, adding: 'The fox will be the first to speak.'

The fox began without any preamble: 'We four chieftains have decided that you must move house, for you're in everybody's way.'

'That's what you say, you cunning rascal!' thought the mole, but out loud he only dared to protest feebly: 'But why? I'm happy where I am, in my wigwam near the old maple tree.'

'Happy or not,' croaked the raven, 'you're all black and ugly. How do you expect us to look at you all the time?'

'Well, you're no beauty yourself!' thought the mole. 'All the bird mothers try to hide from you when they're hatching their young so that they should not take after you.' But before he could say anything, the hare had begun to speak.

'You keep burrowing under the ground all the time, and you don't stop even at night,' he complained. 'Don't you know that I am a very light sleeper and that the noise you make wakes me?'

The mole's clever little eyes, glinting in the bright sunshine, were fixed on the hare's face, and they seemed to be replying:

'Oh, go on with you! Do you expect me to believe that it's me who keeps waking you at night? I should think it's more likely to be your own fear — you've been a coward all your life, and once a coward always a coward.'

But it was just the mole's eyes that made this reply; from his lips there came only an embarrassed apology:

'I'm sorry to hear that, and I promise to go about my work more quietly in future so as not to disturb you.'

Now it was the bear's turn to speak.

'I want to make myself a new trail and your molehill is in my way,' he said in a deep voice. 'I hope you don't think I shall make a detour round it.'

The mole stood there for a while, looking in fright from one to the other. Then, hoping to make them relent and change their minds, he wailed:

'Oh, dear me, what *am* I to do? My father and my grandfather and my great grand-father all lived in that wigwam before me. The great Manitou himself gave them permission to build it where it is. Where am I to go if you chase me out like this?'

'Stop grousing!' the fox barked at him. 'If you don't get out of your own accord we'll kill you one of these days and get rid of you that way.'

'Now what's all this noise?' A strange voice suddenly interrupted their debate. They all turned round in amazement and found a turtle looking at them.

'Get away from here, and be quick about it!' the turtle ordered them angrily. 'This is *my* island, and you have no business here in the first place.'

'But we're having a conference . . .' protested the raven.

'What's that to me?' retorted the turtle. 'Be off with you before I scorch you with hot sand. Goodbye!'

And truly, the sand began to grow hotter and hotter, making the four chieftains withdraw without any more ado; quickly they ran to the shore and swam across to the mainland. Only the mole stayed behind, digging down into the sand where it was not so hot, and not sticking his nose out again until he felt that the coast was clear.

'I see you're very powerful and kind,' he said to the turtle. 'I'd like to ask you a favour.'

'Do. Have no fear, I'll do my best to help you in any way I can. Those four scoundrels wanted to harm you, but I shan't let them. I have a strong carapace and am not the least afraid of them and their weapons.'

'They mean to drive me out of my wigwam and to kill me if I don't obey them and get out voluntarily. Could I perhaps stay here with you?'

'That's hardly possible, for there are no trees here, nor any grass. But I'll tell you what — let's become friends, and as long as we stick loyally to one another, no one will dare to lift a finger against you.'

The mole agreed gladly; the knowledge that he now had a friend to help him filled his heart with confidence and hope. Now he need be afraid no longer. He took leave of the turtle and they parted, promising to visit one another from time to time.

The four chieftains soon got to know that the mole had a friend and protector in the turtle, and they were careful not to interfere with him in any way. But they secretly hoped to be revenged upon him — especially the fox, who conceived a malicious idea.

'Yes, that's it,' he said to himself, 'I must see to it that those two don't meet. And then — we shall see . . .'

On the day when the turtle was supposed to visit the mole, the war drums sounded unexpectedly in the forest, their throbbing reaching as far as the Dry Island where the turtle was just preparing to leave.

'I don't like the sound of that,' thought the turtle, stopping on the shore to wait for the drums to cease.

In the meantime the drumming grew louder and louder, so that it seemed to the mole that the whole world must surely have set out on the war path.

'What on earth can be happening?' the mole asked himself fearfully, peeping out of his wigwam every so often in the hope of seeing the turtle, in whose company he would have felt much easier.

But the turtle did not come.

'Perhaps I'd better climb to the top of the rock — there I'll be more safe than at home,' thought the mole, climbing up to the top of the highest cliff, where he stayed the rest of the day. It was getting dark by the time he made his way back home.

As he went, he met the fox.

'Oh, what a surprise! We were sure you had been burned to death, too,' the fox told him with feigned surprise, his eyes full of cunning and malice.

'Why should I?' wondered the mole.

'Didn't you know? The turtle from the Dry Island was here looking for you, furious because he said you had been slandering him behind his back. You were out, so he burned down your wigwam.'

The mole almost fainted with shock. The world seemed to reel about him. To be thus mistreated by his best friend! The poor fellow thanked the fox for the news and hurried off home, failing to notice the sly smile on the other's face. He spent that night sleeping in the open next to the charred remains of his home, wondering how to avenge himself on his former friend.

Early the next morning he swam across the lake, calling out to the turtle in a shrill voice in which pain intermingled with anger:

'Come out, you traitor, and let's fight to the death!'

But there was silence inside the turtle's wigwam. Looking inside, the mole found that the turtle was away. He had gone out to hunt especially early.

'Well, never mind, I'll give you a taste of your own medicine!' cried the mole indignantly, setting fire to the wigwam. The flames shot up with a dull roar, and smoke soon enveloped the Dry Island.

The turtle hurried back at once. 'Is this how you repay me for my help and friendship?' he called from afar. And he came up to the mole and grappled with him.

They fought long and hard, scattering the sand all round them. In the end the sand became angry and buried them, so that they both perished.

The four chieftains rejoiced at this, for it had been they who had set fire to the mole's wigwam. The fox then had only to put the blame on the turtle, and the simple-minded mole had believed her.

When friends fall out, their enemies rejoice.

The Otter's Friendship

The snow fell unceasingly for many days and nights in the Month of Long Sleep. A wild blizzard galloped all over the country with the wind for a horse, obliterating the tracks of animals, which fled before it to the safety of their dens and hide-outs.

An unwelcome guest — hunger — made himself at home in the villages of the red men, forcing the hunters to go out into the storm; but they always returned empty-handed, weary with the unavailing search for the animal tracks which lay buried deep in the silent white snow.

The howling of hungry wolves could occasionally be heard above the clamour of the wind, chilling the blood of the hunters; nevertheless, the weeping of their hungry children dismayed them still more.

It was then that the tribe's shaman, the mighty Dadahwat, invoked the aid of his magic pouch.

'In it is a powerful charm,' he told the assembled hunters. 'All you have to do is to touch it and it will bring you whatever prey you wish to kill. But take care not to cut out the dead animal's heart and eat it, for then the magic would cease to work.'

The chieftain was the first to touch the magic pouch; he made a wish that he might next day kill a bear. All the other hunters followed suit, the youngest, Skagedi, being last. He wished to kill a lynx.

A frosty night set in. The snowstorm battered at the walls of the dwellings as if it meant to blow them away, and clouds of snow whirled and eddied through the countryside like white apparitions while the wind accompanied their wild dance by its fierce melodies in the tops of the trees.

Skagedi alone was awake that night. Unable to bear the pangs of hunger, he got up while it was still dark and went out into the forest trusting to his memory and hoping to find, in the first light of dawn, a fresh lynx track.

How great was his surprise, though, when he came across a lynx in the dark! The wild beast was holding down with his paw two young otters, which were still alive. They raised their heads on hearing Skagedi's footfall, looking up at him in the starlight with such beseeching expressions that his heart was moved to see them.

He killed the lynx with a single blow and was so overjoyed when the otters ran free that he quite forgot his hunger. But his stomach reasserted itself as soon as the otters vanished from sight. And now he felt so famished that he at once ate the heart of his prey, regardless of the shaman's prohibition. No one will know, he said to himself as he returned home and lay down to sleep. And he dropped off at once into the deepest of slumbers.

In the meantime the men of the village had gone out to hunt, but the charm of the magic pouch had lost its efficacy. The bear got away, although the chieftain had almost caught him, nor did the others fare better.

There's something wrong, they decided, and they ran at once back to the village to consult Dadahwat, who at once guessed that someone must have disobeyed his instructions. They did not have to look far for the culprit — an unskinned lynx lay in front of Skagedi's wigwam, and when the shaman turned him over he saw that the heart had been taken. Skagedi had eaten it!

'The boy must be punished! He destroyed the charm of the pouch which was the envy of all the shamans throughout the Indian country. Manitou himself endowed it with its power.' Thus spoke the angry Dadahwat to the silent crowd of hunters. And he passed an instant verdict on the offender:

'We shall leave for another region, where we'll find hunting grounds rich in game, but you will stay here all alone in the village, without food and clothing, because you have sinned heavily against your friends.'

The punishment was harsh indeed, but Skagedi accepted it like a man. Not one of the hunters spoke a word in his defence, not a single woman gave him a compassionate look. Only little Wia's eyes filled with tears, which ran down her cheeks as she stood there looking at him.

They all left, and Skagedi was alone. He sat for a long time in his wigwam, shivering with cold; not even the fire could give him sufficient warmth any more. As he listened to the raging of the storm outside, it suddenly seemed to him that he heard someone's footfalls. Yes, there was no doubt about it — someone was approaching his wigwam. He looked out but could see no one, yet a soft, kind voice came to him through the blizzard:

'Skagedi, O Skagedi! A few paces away from your wigwam you'll find a bear hiding in the cave. Go and kill him, and you will be saved.'

The voice was heard no more — but Skagedi had heard enough. Next morning, when the wind had abated a little, he left his wigwam and soon reached a cave inside which he found a bear fast asleep. Killing him with a single arrow, Skagedi dragged the carcass to his tent, where he made new clothes and a pair of moccasins for himself from the bear's fur, cutting up and smoking the meat. And that evening, though he was very tired after his

day's hard work, he could not go to sleep for a long time, thinking of his unknown benefactor, who had saved his life with his good and timely advice.

It was midnight by the time he was about to enter the land of dreams, and he again heard the now familiar voice:

'Skagedi, O Skagedi! Wia will visit you tomorrow. Tell her to make the Indians return. And to tell Dadahwat not to be annoyed with you any more, for you know how to restore the charm of his magic pouch.'

Skagedi ran out into the night, but he did not find the unknown adviser. Only the stars were there, silently glittering in the frosty night.

Wia really did come the following day. She had been afraid she would not find Skagedi alive, and her joy knew no bounds. And she was happier still when the boy told her that he could restore the charm of Dadahwat's magic pouch.

Skagedi had, however, made no mention of his strange adventure. And as soon as Wia had left, he resumed his work of the day before. In the evening he lay by the fire, impatient for the night, when he hoped to hear the kind voice again. And so he did.

'Skagedi, O Skagedi! When Dadahwat brings his pouch, take it in your hands. Then ask the hunters, one by one, what animal they wish to catch. Whenever they state their wish, just open the pouch and out will come the strong bear, the fleet-footed stag, or the snow hare—in short, the very animal they have asked for. You yourself make no wish, though. Just take whatever is left in the pouch and bring it to my wigwam. I shan't tell you where it is, but if you do as I tell you, you'll find the way yourself.'

Next day the Indians returned to the village, and the shaman, whom Wia had given Skagedi's message, handed the boy his magic pouch.

'Very well, then—show us what you can do,' he said, watching the boy with very curious eyes.

Skagedi took the pouch and turned to the hunters.

'What animal do you wish to capture?' he asked the chieftain.

'The bear,' was the reply—and out of the pouch came a sleepy bear.

'And you?' Skagedi asked the chieftain's son.

'The stag,' replied he—but no sooner were the words out of his mouth than a fleet-footed stag jumped out of the pouch and lay·down at his feet.

What followed was like a fairy-tale. One after the other the Indians called out their wishes, and Skagedi could hardly keep up with them in opening the pouch to let all the animals out.

Finally he himself put his hand inside. Deep down on the very bottom there lay something soft and furry, and when Skagedi pulled it out he discovered that it was an otter's paw. Quickly he put it back again and, slipping into his snowshoes, set out to find the wigwam of his unknown benefactor.

He did not know which way to go, but the snowshoes guided him in the right direction.

At the end of the forest he found a small round-topped hut. He had never seen it there before and therefore guessed it must be the abode of his unknown friend. He went in.

The hut was empty. Fish remains lay all over the floor, and the boy could smell an otter's scent. Laying the paw down on the ground he hurried out and turned back towards home. He was stopped by a voice calling his name:

'Skagedi!'

The boy turned round, and to his amazement saw that a great lake was now in the spot where the hut had stood just a moment ago.

'O Skagedi! As a reward for your having delivered my children from the lynx's clutches, Dadahwat's pouch will never again lose its magic power. The paw you brought was also mine.'

'Mine, mine, mine,' repeated the echo in the hills.

'But remember, none of you must ever lay otter traps, or you will lose my friendship.'

Only now did Skagedi hear a splash, and on the surface of the lake he saw rings such as are made when an otter jumps into the water.

He waited a little longer in case the otter might appear again, but the surface was calm and unruffled. And at the forest's edge he saw Wia, who hurried forward to meet him.

'Wia! Wia!' he called out, running towards her. He told her the whole story, and repeated it to the others when they got back home.

Never again did the village suffer want, for the red men lived in friendship with the otter, and so Dadahwat's pouch was always full.

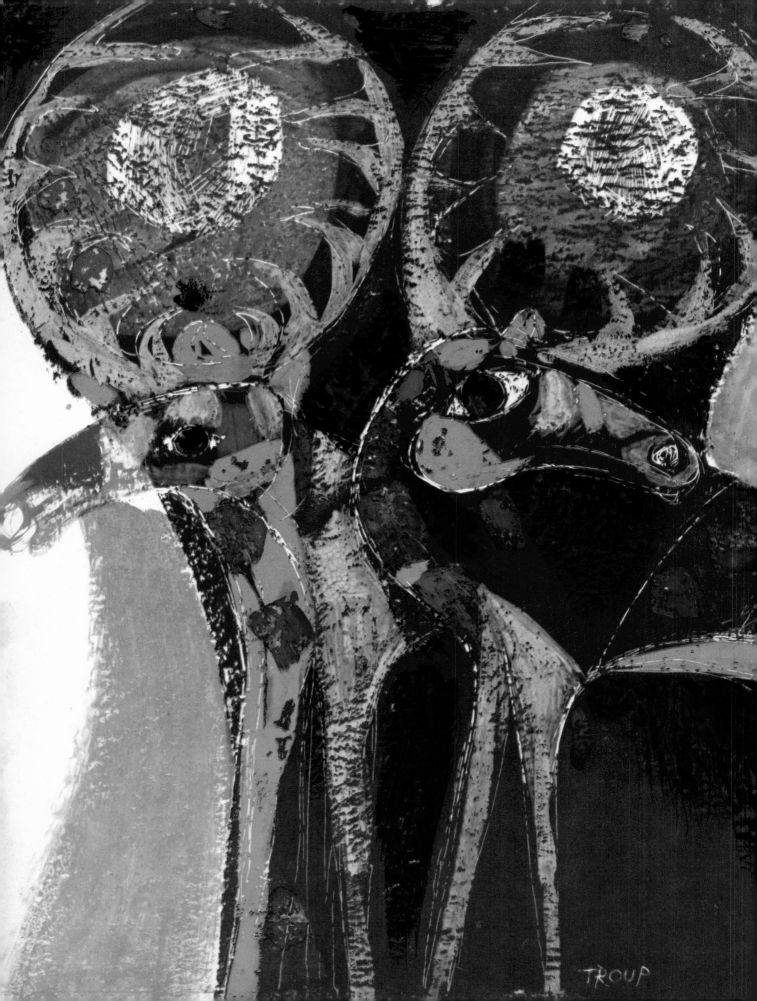

Wolves
and Stags

One day all the wolves of the region met together on the banks of the River Nass to chat and pass the time. There were young cubs, whole packs of adult animals, as well as lone old wolves such as Grey Wolf.

First they sang the long, drawn-out wolf songs, but this resulted in such a great uproar that all the creatures of the woodland took to their heels and fled out of earshot. Some fishes burrowed into the sand and hid under stones; the salmon were not content with this but darted hither and thither, trying to get well away from the source of the unbearable din, until they finally leaped over the rapids and waterfalls, making their way up river.

It was then, they say, that the salmon learned to leap the rapids and overcome every obstacle.

Even the Sun found the howling of the wolves too much for it, set quickly that day and hid its head in the clouds to be out of hearing. On the other hand, the wolves' concert lured the Moon out to the top of the pine trees. The wolves were so pleased to have a listener that they redoubled their efforts.

Soon, however, they grew hoarse and had to find some other means of amusing themselves. And, as is usually the case with a *potlach*, long-forgotten tales of heroism were now recounted. Old warriors showed the wolf cubs their scars, received in many famous battles. Thus they sat long into the night, talking and gossiping, until the mist began to rise over the river and a new day was about to dawn.

The stags now gathered on the opposite bank. The mist had carried the wolves' tales to their ears, and they had to laugh in spite of themselves, for animals only believe the words of their own kin.

'Who dares to poke fun at the brave wolves?' came indignantly from the other side of the river.

But still the stags laughed, as if they would never stop. Hidden in the morning mist they felt no fear of the wolves. Then the Sun jumped up into the sky, rubbed its eyes, and at once the mist disappeared.

'Hullo there, stags!' the wolves shouted across the river. 'You don't even know how to laugh properly! Look!' And they bared their teeth, which glinted evilly in the sunlight. 'Ha, ha, ha!' they laughed, raising an echo in the forest.

'Now it's our turn!' called out the stags. 'Mmmm . . . mmm . . . mm . . .' they tried to laugh through closed mouths. This set the wolves laughing even more uproariously.

'Ha, ha, ha!' they screamed. 'You've got to open your mouths if you want to laugh correctly.'

'Mmmmm . . . mmm . . . mm!' the stags muttered again, showing their almost toothless gums. So that's why they can't laugh properly, thought the wolves, their mouths watering at the sight of such easy prey. In a flash they were in the water, swimming to the other side. The stags waited no longer and fled, but the wolves did not lose their scent and they are pursuing them to this day.

Since that time the wolves have known that stags cannot defend themselves against their fangs and that they are easy prey.

The Rabbit
and
the Wildcat

The wildcat was extremely hungry and, as luck would have it, she could not catch as much as a mouse. She was therefore just getting ready to raid the Indian village below the Windy Rock, to see what she could find there, when she stumbled over a sleeping rabbit.

She could hardly believe her eyes. There he was, taking a nap in the noonday heat, his whiskers fluttering with his snores. Such easy game!

'Wakey, wakey!' the wildcat cried, placing her paw on the rabbit's back. The poor creature awoke with a start — and at once wished he were a thousand miles away.

'You ought to thank me for waking you because it's bad for your health to be sleeping in the sun like this,' the wildcat told him. 'But I'm afraid I'll have to eat you now, for I'm terribly hungry.'

The rabbit began to shake with fright. 'If only you leave me alone I'll tell you about some much better prey. How about it?' he cajoled.

'Well, we shall see,' replied the wildcat, but she nevertheless pressed him down a little harder in case he meant to deceive her and run away.

Just then they heard some noises from not far off.

'Hear that?' said the rabbit. 'Turkeys. Their path is just a few yards away. You would never find it by yourself, but I'll take you to it.'

The wildcat thought this a good idea. 'Don't be too sure I'll spare you,' she told him all the same. But the rabbit knew that the danger had passed.

'Come on, we mustn't delay,' he urged her, striking while the iron was hot. 'Hurry!'

'Oh, they'll run away before we get there anyway,' said the wildcat doubtfully.

'Of course they won't. You must lie down across their path as if you were dead — then you can take your time and make your choice. Just follow me, and don't make any noise,'

Like a couple of shadows they crept through the long grass, and in a few moments they came across the turkey path.

'You lie down here,' advised the rabbit, 'and pretend to be dead. The turkeys are coming.'

The wildcat quickly did as he told her, stretching herself out across the path and closing her eyes. The rabbit went forward to meet the turkeys. It was good timing for he met them at the first turning.

'Gowa!' he greeted them. 'I have just killed a wildcat.'

The turkeys did not believe him. 'Seeing is believing,' said their chieftain. 'Come and show us.'

'It's only a few steps away from here. But if you're afraid, you should not go any farther . . .'

Of course, no turkey would think of admitting to a rabbit that he was afraid of anything. And so they walked on, in Indian file, until they reached the spot where the wildcat lay, shamming death.

'I've sent her to the Eternal Hunting-grounds with my tomahawk,' boasted the rabbit.

The turkeys gobbled in admiration, unable to look their fill at the wildcat. They had never had an opportunity of examining one at such close quarters before.

The rabbit stepped back a little and, from a safe distance, waited to see what would happen. He did not have long to wait. Suddenly the wildcat lashed out with her paw and, seizing the fattest turkey-hen, darted up into the nearest tree with her.

The turkeys scattered to every side, gobbling angrily at the cunning wildcat and the treacherous rabbit.

'We'll avenge ourselves,' decided the turkey chieftain, red with rage, when the turkeys again flocked together in a clearing. He then picked a number of the strongest warriors and without a moment's delay set out with them in pursuit of the rabbit.

The rabbit had already forgotten all about the matter and was happily munching grass. When he saw the horribly painted turkey warriors approaching he took to his heels, racing to evade his pursuers. He ran through the bushes, and the turkeys ran after him. He jumped over a stream, but the turkeys were still at his heels. Then he thought of hiding in the badger's den. But before he could get inside, the turkey chieftain caught up with him and stepped hard on his tail, tearing it off. Thus the rabbit lost his long tail, and he sat sadly inside the badger's den looking at the little stump that was all he had left of it. The turkeys put the rabbit's tail at the end of a long pole like a scalp and bore it off in triumph.

The rabbit, however, did not worry overmuch about his loss. And he soon found that his short tail made it easier for him to run, and so he has kept it to this day.

But he could not forgive the wildcat for leaving him in the lurch as she had done, and he thought of ways and means of getting even with her.

He soon received an opportunity. The very next day he was running about on the road when he heard someone snoring. Going on to investigate, he found a mustang enjoying an afternoon nap. He was sleeping so soundly that the rabbit was sure he would not wake for some time.

He therefore hurried to the tree in which the wildcat had her home.

'Hey there!' he called out. 'Are you in?'

'Here I am,' the wildcat replied. 'What do you want?'

The rabbit lowered his voice and went on: 'I know of big prey. Come on down and I'll whisper it to you.'

The wildcat jumped down from her branch.

'Well, go on, tell me about it,' she said, quivering with impatience.

'There's a dead mustang in the roadway and no one has yet spotted him,' the rabbit told her. 'I'm a vegetarian myself and don't eat flesh, so I at once thought of you.'

'Let's not waste any more time, then,' cried the wildcat, conjuring up visions of the wonderful feasts she would have for a long time to come. And she hurried after the rabbit.

The mustang was still asleep.

'We can't leave him here like this,' the rabbit said. 'I know what we'll do, though — I'll tie him to your tail. Turn round.'

The rabbit then tied the wildcat's and the mustang's tails together, tying them with the firmest rabbit's knots.

'There, that's done it!' he told the wildcat. 'And now you can take him home.'

The wildcat pulled for all she was worth.

The mustang woke up and tried to get to his feet. The wildcat screamed in terror. This frightened the mustang, who thought it must surely be the devil himself clutching him. And he galloped down the road as fast as he knew how.

The wildcat screeched and wailed, making the mustang run faster and faster to escape the devil at his tail. Soon they both vanished in the dust.

The rabbit laughed till he could laugh no more.

'A few nice lumps on your head will teach you a lesson,' he said to the absent wildcat — and he ran off in search of fresh adventure.

How the Snake
Got his
Poison Fangs

This happened shortly after the almighty Cipas had created the animals, giving them everything they needed for life: the eagle his powerful wings, the stag his swift legs, and the bear his great strength. Only the snake Kasur was left defenceless. All he could do was to try and catch flies, but even these made fun of him and molested him, for he did not have a single tooth.

The rabbit, who was otherwise anything but a hero, also tormented the snake in various ways, burying him in the sand or throwing him in the river. It was a minor miracle that Kasur survived all these adversities and did not perish as a result. Being patient and wise, he knew that only the great Cipas could help him.

Thus, when all the other animals were asleep, he crawled to the Creator's abode. He travelled all night, over many big rocks which barred his way, and by morning had reached the huge cave.

A sacred fire was burning in the middle, its fragrant smoke filling the air with a heady scent. Cipas himself sat by the fire, and he fixed the snake with a penetrating eye.

'Why dost thou come to me?' he asked.

'I am most unhappy,' explained the snake. 'I am unable to defend myself when others hurt me or make fun of me, having neither the strength to fight them, nor the speed to escape. Nor yet am I so small as to be able to hide from my enemies. Only you can help me — otherwise I am sure to die.'

'Yes, I shall help thee,' said the Creator. 'Come closer . . .'

Kasur crawled right up to the fire. Cipas rose to his feet, enveloped himself in smoke, and uttered a few magic words. Then, still reciting his incantation, he picked up several red-hot embers and wrapped them in some short sunrays which he broke off for the purpose.

'Open thy mouth,' he instructed the snake.

At once Kasur felt teeth sharp as needles grow in his mouth.

'Now thou hast a truly terrible weapon. Thy fangs are poisoned, so that whoever they bite must perish. With such a weapon thou wilt find it easy to defend thyself.'

And with these words Cipas carried Kasur outside and returned to the sacred fire in his cave.

The snake crawled slowly homewards, not trying to hide any more, for he no longer had anything to fear. On the way he met the rabbit.

'Ah, look who's here!' shouted the rabbit from afar. 'My old friend Kasur! And where are you off to, if I may ask?'

'I'm on my way home,' replied the snake, and tried to avoid the rabbit.

'Don't you want to play?' said the rabbit, standing in his path and suddenly plunging his sharp teeth into the snake's back.

'Leave me alone, or you'll be sorry!' Kasur warned him.

'Ho, ho!' laughed the rabbit. 'That's rich — surely you don't think I'm afraid of you, do you?'

Without any more warning the snake struck out at his tormentor, and, before the rabbit knew what was happening, killed him with his poison fangs. Then he continued calmly on his way.

The rabbit's death created panic in the animal world. Everyone gave Kasur a wide berth, and they wondered who had made him so powerful.

'I know,' said the frog. 'It was Cipas himself who did it.'

There was a brief silence, and then someone — who it was it is now hard to say — shouted out:

'Let's go and kill Cipas!'

'Yes, let's! Let's kill Cipas!' cried the others, starting out in the direction of the cave where Cipas lived.

Kasur wasted no time and, knowing the route better than they did, managed to reach the cave before them and warn Cipas of what was in the offing.

'We must fly at once,' decided Cipas. 'There's a path leading underground from this cave, and there I'll be safe . . .'

By this time the animals had reached the cave and were making a fearful din outside.

'Quickly, Kasur! Take me on your back and go as fast as you can.'

Cipas raised his hand, uttered a magic formula, and a deep, seemingly bottomless pit opened up in front of them. As soon as they had entered it, the earth closed over their heads, leaving no trace of the opening.

The pursuers burst into the cave and stopped in their tracks, dumbfounded. The cave was completely empty. They looked everywhere but found nothing — the Creator was gone, and they had to go back to their homes disappointed.

This explains how it came about that Cipas had to flee to the dark underground world; and though he sent Kasur back to earth, he himself has never returned and lives there to this day.

When he yawns the volcanoes belch forth smoke, ashes come out of the craters, and the hot lava pours down into the valleys. And when he moves, there are earthquakes with rocks splitting and mountains toppling, the rivers rising and flooding the countryside, people as well as animals being possessed by fear and terror.

The Skunk
and the Evil
Spirit

An evil manitou called Long Claw used to live at the very end of the Indian country. He was a truly dangerous evil spirit, able to kill anyone he pleased with his claws. He had the strength of a bear, whom he closely resembled, except for his extraordinarily long, purple-coloured claws.

The only thing Long Claw could not do was swim, and for that reason those whom he attacked, whether they were Indians or animals, always sought refuge in the water, and many indeed were thus able to save themselves.

Nevertheless, they were all afraid of him — all, that is, with the exception of a small, insignificant animal.

Who was this fearless creature?

It was the skunk, who made a point of wandering about in the vicinity of Long Claw's cave in order to measure forces with him.

One day they really did meet, outside the skunk's lair. He was sitting on a tree-stump, smoking a pipe, and Long Claw came by, looking for prey.

'Ha!' cried the evil spirit. 'Fear me!'

The skunk did not so much as move an eyelid. He just went on sitting there and smoking as if nothing had happened.

'Hoo, hoo! Run, if you value your life!' Long Claw yelled, waving his arms about in front of the skunk's nose.

'Get out of the way, you monster!' said the skunk calmly, taking the pipe out of his mouth. 'I'm watching the grass grow and you come along and stamp on it.'

'Wha-a-at?' shouted the evil spirit. 'Oohoo, oohoo! What did you say, you impudent little worm? I'll tear you apart and make tassels to my moccasins out of you! Oohoo! I'll devour you like a ripe plum. Fear me, go on, fear me!'

'Not on your life!' retorted the skunk.

'You won't? What do you mean by it? I'll flatten you like an Indian shield! Look!' Long Claw picked up a huge stone and with a single blow broke it into a hundred fragments.

'Is that all?' said the skunk contemptuously, filling up his pipe. 'Very well, then, if you really insist on scrapping with me, I have no objection.' And he jumped down from his tree-stump. 'What are the rules?'

'I'll send you to the Eternal Hunting-grounds with a mere four blows,' boasted Long Claw.

'All right, you can have the first four, and then I'll start in on you.'

'You won't live long enough to do that,' promised Long Claw. He spread his legs wide and hit out at the skunk for the first time.

It was a terrible blow, and it knocked the skunk into the ground up to his knees. Before he had recovered from it, Long Claw dealt him a second, and then a third, which left only the skunk's head above the ground.

Bang! came the fourth blow, and the skunk disappeared in the deep hole.

'You wait till I get out!' he shouted up at the evil spirit. 'I'll pay you back—with interest!'

'What can you do to hurt me?' laughed Long Claw; but he was a little disconcerted at finding that his adversary was still alive.

'Well, I shan't hit you,' the skunk told him. 'I shan't so much as lift a finger against you. All I have to do is to walk round you four times in succession.'

'You don't think that worries me, do you?' Long Claw said scornfully. 'You can walk round me as many times as you like — I'll take a snooze in the meantime.'

And he stretched out comfortably on the ground. The skunk took a pinch of some spice from his tobacco pouch and filled his pipe with it, muttering an incantation.

Then he started walking round the evil spirit. 'Are you afraid of me?' he asked on his first round.

'Not a bit,' replied Long Claw sleepily.

'Anonani, Anonani, out you come!' murmured the skunk.

At that moment a cloud of smoke came billowing out of his pipe, and the evil spirit was immediately enveloped in it; but, what was worse, a terrible, odious smell filled his eyes and mouth and lungs, and try as he would, he could not be rid of it.

'Oohoo! Oohoo!' he shouted, jumping up in great pain. 'You've killed me!' And he fell lifeless to the ground.

The skunk was overjoyed at his victory. As a souvenir, he cut off the evil spirit's long claws and made himself a necklace out of them.

He wanted to show it to all his neighbours, but wherever he went he was accompanied by Anonani, the terrible smell, which made everyone run away from him. And so it is only the skunk tribe who know about their ancestor's famous fight with Long Claw, the evil spirit. They are the only ones who don't mind Anonani, but, on the contrary, find him a useful ally who protects them against their enemies.

The Strawberries

An Indian and his squaw lived in a small wigwam by the Grumbling Brook. Perhaps it was because the brook kept up a constant plashing or because the wind was always whistling through the clefts of the Wailing Rock that the man was of a very quarrelsome disposition and, as opposed to his silent companions, so very talkative that he gabbled away from morning till night.

He did not stop talking even when he went hunting. As he lay in wait for a stag, he would jeer at a magpie sitting on a bough above his head, and so it was no wonder that all the deer gave the place a wide berth, what with so much noise going on all the time.

His wife was the worst sufferer, though, not having a moment of peace with him, for the wretch cried out angrily even in his sleep.

It is said that one should wear a pair of moccasins for as long as they last. The squaw also could only bear it for so long, and then one day she lost her patience with her stubborn, bad-tempered husband and decided to leave him. As she did not know where to go, she just walked along the Grumbling Brook, following the Sun.

The Indian soon found that his wife had left him, but in his pig-headedness he thought she would come back before long, and got ready to give her a good talking to.

A day passed, then two days, and three. On the morning of the fourth the Indian went to ask the Grumbling Brook for advice, but all he could hear instead of a proper reply was 'Follow the Sun, follow the Sun,' and so he set out in the direction the brook had indicated.

'The Grumbling Brook is right,' the Sun told him, 'your squaw is following me and doesn't want to have any more to do with you.'

The Indian's soul filled with sorrow. 'I'll never quarrel with her again,' he promised, 'only please tell her to come back to me.'

'Well, I don't know,' replied the Sun. 'However, if you really mean to keep your word, I'll see what I can do. And now meet her halfway.'

The man did not hesitate, but ran forward following her tracks. He travelled all day and all night, not stopping to eat or sleep, but even so he would hardly have caught up with his squaw had not the mighty chieftain Sun helped him.

The squaw journeyed eastwards and had forgotten all about her husband.

'I must make her look back — that's the only way she'll remember him,' thought the Sun. 'And she'll only look back at something she has never seen before. Yes, that's it — I'll grow some blackberries.'

At that moment a blackberry bush grew alongside the path, full of tempting black fruit, but the woman never even noticed it.

'Perhaps she'll care for blueberries, then,' said the Sun and prepared yet another surprise for her.

No one could be expected to pass by such wonderful blueberries, yet the squaw hurried past without stopping.

'I don't think I have anything else that is new,' thought the Sun dejectedly, but then lit up with a delighted smile. 'Why, of course — strawberries! How could I have forgotten about them?'

Quickly the Sun chose the finest, largest and choicest strawberries, sprinkled them with morning dew, and planted them by the wayside.

The squaw halted, her attention caught by the delicious smell of fresh strawberries. 'What's making this sweet smell, I wonder?' she said to herself, and then she saw the strawberries. She could not resist the temptation, and so she knelt down and started picking them. When she had picked them all, she stood up and looked round. In the meantime the clever Sun had planted strawberries in the spots she had just passed, thus making her go back a little, picking the lovely red fruit as she went. And as she did so she suddenly felt homesick and wished she were back with her husband.

Now she no longer wanted to run away but, on the contrary, her only desire was to be home again. Making a bunch of the finest and tastiest strawberries for her husband, she set out on her return journey. And before the Grumbling Brook grew pink with the reflection of the evening clouds, she met the Indian coming in the opposite direction, breathless and tired from his travels.

They were both very happy to see each other and, joining hands, walked slowly back to the Wailing Rock, where I am told they live peacefully and happily to this day.

And the strawberries? Why, they have spread all over the Indian country, so that everyone can taste their sweet fruit.

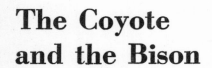

The Coyote
and the Bison

A coyote once found the skull of a bison. It lay there on the prairie, bleached white by the Sun, and no one had thought of taking any notice of it before.

The coyote was an inquisitive old busybody, and he examined the strange object from all sides. There is sure to be a treasure inside, it occurred to him, and he looked round for a stone with which to break it open.

He should not have done that. At the first blow the bones crumbled to dust, which was all he found of the imagined treasure. But hearing the thundering noise of many hooves he looked up, and trembled with terror: a strip of red dust on the horizon told him that a herd of bison was coming towards him.

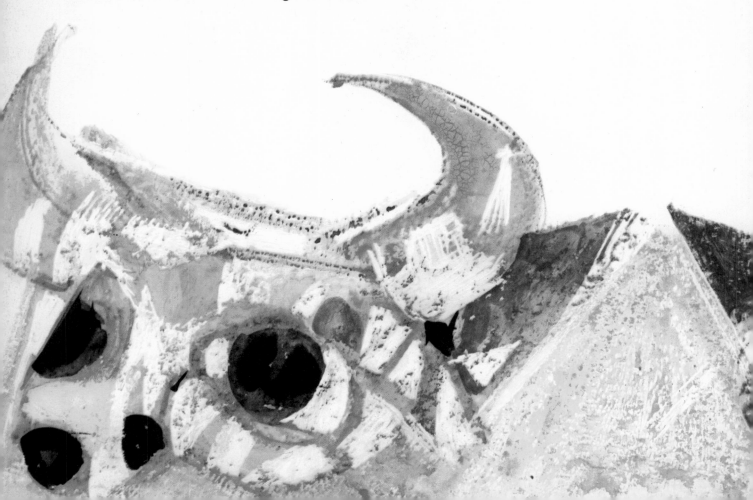

The coyote started running round in desperate circles, pleading: 'Oh, good spirits, help me, help me! Change me into a tree-stump!'

Instantly a small, hollow tree-stump stood there in place of the coyote. The herd rumbled past, taking not the slightest notice of him, but the last bison of all stumbled over the tree-stump and became infuriated. The bison lowered his massive head and rushed at the offending stump.

'Oh, good spirits, change me into a stone!' pleaded the coyote again.

But even this did not help, for he felt a terrible blow, and then saw the enraged bison stand on his hind legs in readiness to stamp the stone out of existence.

'Oh, good spirits, change me into a bush!' the coyote begged, and the spirits helped him once more.

All the bison's strength now proved of no avail; the thorns of the bush pricked his skin and he could not get at the roots.

'Let's make peace,' he suggested finally. 'Show me your true likeness and we'll be friends.'

The coyote at once jumped out of the bush, afraid that the bison might yet change his mind, and handed him the peace pipe.

'Yes, let's be friends,' agreed the bison. 'But I need your help.'

'A pleasure, I'm sure,' replied the coyote. 'What can I do for you?'

'The herd has stolen two cows from me. You must sharpen my horns, and then we'll set out on the warpath together.'

'I am a good warrior and have many scalps at home,' boasted the coyote. 'You'll do well to join forces with me.' And he sharpened the bison's horns really well, being very adept at this sort of thing.

'I'll be your scout,' he offered then, running up a nearby hill and looking round.

The bison herd slept not far away.

'Quick, quick!' the coyote cried. 'Our enemies are asleep, let's take them by surprise!'

The bison snorted and charged forward. The coyote, on the other hand, was in no hurry to join the fray, preferring to hide and await the outcome.

He hardly dared to breathe as the battle broke out near him, the earth trembling with the impact of charging hooves and the air splitting with the noise of horns crashing against each other.

Then there was silence again, and the coyote heard someone hurrying towards him. Looking out of his hiding-place he found it was the bison coming back with the two cows.

'A good job you've come!' the coyote cried. 'I have already spent all my arrows, shooting at your adversaries.'

'I didn't see you do any shooting,' replied the bison doubtfully.

'Didn't I just! At least four times I saved you from being scalped,' the coyote lied, quite unabashed. 'Now you must share your booty with me.'

And, willy-nilly, the bison had to give the coyote the smaller of the two cows.

The cunning rascal was looking forward to a nice, large bison steak, and he was in a hurry to leave.

'Manitou be with you, my friend,' he told the bison in parting. 'I see you are busy and so I shan't keep you any longer.'

Before the bison could reply, the coyote had vanished with the cow in the tall grass.

He waited only long enough for his friend's footfalls to die down in the distance, then he quickly killed and skinned the cow. This was hard work and he was tired, so he said to himself:

'I'd better take a nap before I have my feast — I'm all done in.'

He accordingly curled up on the ground, and soon he was snoring so prodigiously that the prairie undulated with the sound of it. He dreamed how clever and cunning he was, far more clever than all the rest of the animals put together.

But unfortunately for him, this time it was only a dream. While he slept, a pack of wolves came that way, and when he woke up all that was left of the cow was a heap of gnawed bones. He flew into a terrible rage.

'What thief has dared to do this to me?' he shouted indignantly. But the prairie answered him with a profound silence.

Feeling famished, he thought he might as well make the best of a bad job by sucking the marrow from the bones, since that was all he had left. 'I know what I'll do! I'll find myself a stone and use it to get at the marrow.'

He was not to have even that much, however. Before he came back with the stone, a badger came along and sucked all the marrow from the bones, not leaving the slightest bit.

What now? The coyote sat there, dejected and hungry, his ears and tail hanging, a picture of misery.

'Perhaps I can beat the bones to a powder,' it occurred to him. He struck out with his stone, and the bones broke and scattered all over the place.

'If only you had a beak, if only you had a beak!' shouted someone above his head.

Looking up he found several crows hovering in the air.

'You couldn't have come at a more opportune moment,' the coyote told them and, putting his paws together, pleaded: 'Please peck the bones to powder, and I'll give you half of it.'

'Very well, very well. Just find a spoon, just find a spoon,' said the oldest of the crows.

The coyote obeyed and went: it did not take him long, as he was lucky enough to find a spoon only a little way distant, on an abandoned Indian camp site.

Running back he had to swallow his saliva and his legs almost gave way under him, so hungry was he by now. But a third time unlucky — he found neither bones nor powder, only the crows flying about, their beaks completely white.

'Ha, ha, ha! Caw, caw, caw!' they shrieked.

The coyote flung the spoon up at them furiously.

If only he could at least hit one of them, the thieving wretches!

'How stupid, how stupid! Caw, caw!' was the reply from above his head.

There was nothing left for the coyote to do but to run off as fast as he knew how, trying to outrun his disgrace, which seemed to stick to him like a shadow.

The Magpie's Nest

The people who inhabited the Indian country built hundreds of wigwams, every one different from all the others. The animals came and looked at them curiously, the bear praising the thoroughness with which they had been built, the wildcat wishing she might go and warm herself by the fire inside. But it was the birds who were the most intrigued, for they had never seen anything like it before.

They gathered round, twittering and quacking and cawing. And then it occurred to them that they, too, ought to build such dwellings. The eagle, who was their chieftain, welcomed this idea and gave orders that they should all start work at once.

It was then, at the beginning of spring, that the birds first learned how to build nests. The woodpecker went about it like a real carpenter, drumming on the tree trunk with his powerful beak until the chips flew, taking time off every now and again to examine his handiwork, and then starting anew. The swifts and the swallows built their nests of mud, just like the dwellings of the southern Indians. But it was the hummingbird who produced the loveliest nest of all. Not only was it more expertly put together than that of the swallows, the hummingbird even decorated it with moss. With the finest and greenest moss he could find.

Yet not all the birds proved equally diligent and conscientious. The owl merely found a hollow cleft in the rock, threw in a handful of rubbish, and settled down to sleep. The quail, on the other hand, made itself comfortable in the grass and waited blithely for it to grow and form a shelter over its head. And the magpie did nothing at all, just strolling about the woods and gossiping. When the other birds asked her why she did not build a nest, she replied:

'I don't know how. And why should I, anyway? I can always find some branch or other to spend the night on.' And with these words the magpie flew off, to pass the time of day chattering somewhere else.

A few sleeps later they were all finished with their work, all except the magpie, of course. The Great Spirit, who had watched them as they busied themselves with their nest-building, came out of his wigwam in the sky and addressed the bird nation:

'I am very pleased with the diligence you have shown, and I intend to reward you for your endeavour.'

The Great Spirit took four eagle feathers from his head-dress, summoned the four winds—the East Wind and the West Wind, the South Wind and the North Wind—and gave them one feather each, saying:

'Before the Morning Star disappears over the horizon of the Great Water, I want all the birds' nests over which you'll pass to be filled with eggs, giving rise to a new bird generation . . .'

The voice of the Great Spirit could still be heard dying away high up among the clouds when the four feathers, carried by the four winds, set out on their long journey. And as they flew above the Indian country, they filled all the birds' nests with eggs—snow white and yellow, reddish and spotted eggs, according to the kind of fledglings that were to come out of them.

The birds were overjoyed. Some were already sitting on the eggs, others were still waiting to receive this gift from the Great Spirit. The magpie grew very sad, for she realised too late that she had been wrong to be so lazy, and she started frantically to build herself a nest. But, of course, she did not have the slightest idea how to go about it, and so she asked everyone she met to come and help. She lamented so pitifully that the other birds felt sorry for her and did their best to help her.

The woodpecker brought her a few splinters, the swifts flew up quickly with some moss and the pigeon collected several blades of grass. The magpie carried all she was given to the top of a tall pine, dumping it down higgledy-piggledy, so that she managed to finish the nest before the wind brought the feather from the Great Spirit's head-dress. And now she only waited to see with how many eggs the Great Spirit would reward her.

Early the next morning, as soon as the first light of dawn coloured the sky red, the birds left their nests all over the Indian country, calling on one another and boasting of their eggs or of their newly hatched fledglings. They were puzzled to find that the magpie was nowhere to be seen.

'She must surely have met with some accident,' they decided at last, for the magpie was always out long before this, gossiping and chattering with one and all. Full of curiosity, they flocked to the pine in which the magpie had made her home.

There a strange sight awaited them: over the top of the most untidy nest they had ever seen they could catch momentary glimpses of the magpie's head or wing or tail as she kept moving about inside, exclaiming angrily all the time:

'One, two, three . . . no, two! Now, really, this is a bit much! I'll never be able to count them like this!' And the magpie again stuck out a dishevelled head.

Now all the birds understood what was happening: the magpie was trying to count her eggs, which turned out to be an impossible task in such an untidy nest. At last the eagle spoke up and told her:

'Serve you right for being so lazy! If you'd built your nest properly, like the rest of us, you'd now be sharing our joy at the gift bestowed on us by the Great Spirit.'

The eagle finished his speech and took off, followed by the entire bird nation. In vain did the magpie call after them, begging them to come and help her put her nest in order and count the eggs.

And that is why the magpie to this day has the ugliest nest of all birds, and why she probably still does not know how many eggs there are in it.

The Raven
and the Whale

It might perhaps seem that most of the adventures which animals had in the country of the Indians concerned the rascally coyote or the rabbit. But there was yet another well-known adventurer out there in the West, and this was the raven. This is the story that is told about his adventure with a whale.

The raven had for a long time wanted to taste the flesh of the whale, but how was he to capture such an enormous creature?

'I'll tie it up and then kill it!' he boasted to himself. And, flying out into the prairie, he borrowed a long, stout lasso and waited for the whale to come close to the shore.

It was not until noon that the colossal beast made its appearance. It was as long as the tallest of trees, and it puffed so vigorously that the rocks on the shore shook with the noise.

The raven picked up the lasso and threw it, catching the whale in the noose. But he could not match the whale for strength; before the bird had time to realise what was happening, the whale had pulled him down and, opening its huge maw, swallowed him, lasso and all.

'How dark it is here!' said the raven feeling his way about the whale's insides as if he were in a maze. 'I must make a fire and take a look round.' He seemed to be in a dark cavern whose walls kept contracting and expanding all the time, while in the middle a large boulder seemed to be rising and falling . . .

'What can it be?' wondered the raven. Hopping closer, he pecked inquisitively at the boulder.

'Ouch!' yelled the whale in a mighty voice. 'Leave my heart alone!'

'So that's what it is!' thought the raven, pecking away at the heart for all he was worth until it stopped beating.

'Aagh!' groaned the whale for the last time and turned over on its back. The raven turned a somersault, and the fire went out.

'I've won!' he rejoiced, but his elation did not last long. How was he to get out? In vain he pecked and pecked at the walls of his prison—he could make no headway at all.

'Caw, caw!' he called out in the hope that someone might hear him outside.

Some children were playing together on the shore, and they heard the raven's call. Seeing the dead whale, they ran home to the village to tell their parents about it. Before long the Indians came with knives and spears, and the raven heard their excited voices. Then there were other sounds to be heard as the men began to peel long strips of blubber from the whale's body.

Soon the spears pierced right inside the whale. The raven waited for the opening to become large enough, and then flew out past the astonished Indians, settling on the bough of a pine tree in a nearby wood.

He had no sooner put his disarrayed plumage in order and recovered a little from his adventure than he began to envy the Indians.

'Well, I like that!' he cried indignantly. 'I fought and killed that whale, and now they just come and eat it up. Caw, caw! I must do something about it!'

He jumped off the bough, gathered some grass and moss with which he made a long beard and hair, making himself up to look like an old magician. Providing himself with a stick and hobbling along with its aid, he then made his way to the village.

He knocked on the door of the first dwelling.

'I am a mighty magician from the hills,' he said when he had entered. 'The spirits have told me that you are in great danger. I have therefore come to warn you.'

'What kind of danger?' asked a young warrior sitting nearest the entrance.

'The dead whale is a harbinger of death,' replied the raven-magician. 'You must quickly take to your boats and sail out to sea. There, it cannot harm you. If any of you remain behind, however . . .' He paused, inclining his head to one side as if listening to the words of invisible spirits. 'If any remain behind, they are truly lost. I can smell death in the air. Hurry, if you value your lives!'

The Indians did not need to be told twice—in a flash they had spread the terrible news throughout the village, and shortly their boats were pulling away from the shore.

The raven stood next to the whale's body, waving his stick in the air as if chasing away death.

As soon as the Indian boats had disappeared over the horizon his behaviour changed. Discarding his disguise he looked with pleasure at the mountain of flesh in front of him and, choosing the choicest bits, sang merrily:

'*Caw, caw, caw! Hee, hee, hee!*
All this meat, just for me!'

How the Opossum
Lost the Hairs on his Tail

Today it would be hard to imagine that such an animal as the opossum might possibly have hairs on his tail. And yet that is just what he did have in times long gone by. In those days the opossum had a beautiful, bushy tail, just like a squirrel's.

The opossum was very proud of his tail and kept looking at it all the time, cherishing it like the most precious of talismans.

He thought he had just about the most wonderful tail in the world. And then one day he met the raccoon. *His* tail was not only well kept and smooth but it was ornamented with a number of dark rings spaced out at regular intervals.

'What a fine tail you have there,' the opossum said to start the conversation.

'Mhm,' replied the raccoon a little irritably, for he was just looking for something to eat and the opossum obviously wanted to chat.

'What a fine tail!' cried the opossum, hopping about excitedly.

'Well, you have a fine one yourself,' said the raccoon, trying to put an end to the talk.

'Yes, I know, only it hasn't got those lovely rings,' said the opossum. 'Couldn't you give me just a tiny bit of yours?'

'No, of course not!' cried the raccoon, pulling in his tail for fear of losing it. There was no trusting such a crazy fellow.

'All right, at least tell me how you got your beautiful rings.'

'Certainly,' replied the raccoon, his eyes glinting with mischief. 'All you have to do is to put some rings made out of tree-bark on your tail and then stick it in the fire. The longer you leave it in, the lovelier will the rings be.'

'Oh, thank you, brother!' cried the opossum, and began to peel off the bark of the nearest tree.

The raccoon was glad to have got rid of the pest. 'Rings indeed!' he muttered under his breath as he slowly trod the raccoon path leading down to the stream where he wanted to catch some fish for his supper.

The opossum was in the meantime putting bark rings on his tail. It was quite a difficult job, and he swore and cursed as he struggled to get it done. If his tail had been as long as a crocodile's, he would surely have burst with rage before he had finished; but luckily his tail was shorter, and so he managed at last to get to the tip. Then he quickly gathered some brushwood, set fire to it, and waited a little for the flames to grow higher.

And then, clamping his teeth firmly together, he put his beringed tail in the fire.

He felt a terrible pain, but said nothing and did not budge. When he saw dark circles in front of his eyes, he told himself: 'Such as these I'll soon have on my tail. The fire is already painting them for me.'

And with this thought he endured his suffering.

At last the fire went out. The opossum crawled away to cool his tail in the moist grass and, groaning with pain, turned his head to see. He was so eager to feast his eyes on his newly acquired ornament.

Not only were there no rings on his tail — all his hairs had, of course, been burned away. As it was, he could consider himself lucky to have any tail left at all.

But he was quite devoid of sense. First he began to cry, then he cursed the raccoon for having tricked him, and finally he ran away to hide.

And though the story got around and many pitied him, the opossum has not ceased to be ashamed of his bare tail to this day, and so he prefers to lie low and does not like to be seen.

The
Beaver
and the
Porcupine

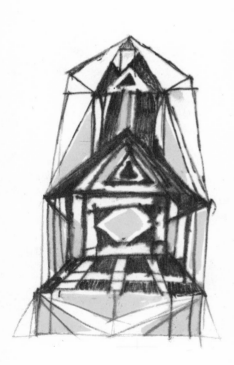

There is a good reason for the enmity that exists between two inhabitants of the banks of the Great Water—the beaver and the porcupine.

They actually started out as being the best of friends. The porcupine lived alone in a cave, and whenever he was out travelling he liked to stop for a chat with the beaver. They gossiped about everything under the Sun, discussing all the latest news, and every now and again holding a *potlach* at which they feasted and exchanged gifts.

And it was at one such meeting at the beaver's dam that some evil spirit put the beaver up to a fine piece of wickedness.

'You know what?' he said suddenly to the porcupine. 'Let's go and play.'

The porcupine was rather surprised at the idea of playing on a full stomach, but nevertheless he agreed:

'All right, but where then shall we play? You haven't got too much space in here, you know.'

'Why, in the water, of course,' replied the beaver. 'Let's dive under.'

The porcupine shivered and said: 'Oh, that's no good, I'm afraid. I can't swim.'

'Never mind, I'll carry you on my back,' suggested the beaver, and little as he liked the whole business, the porcupine climbed obediently on to the other's broad back so as not to offend his host.

As soon as the porcupine had got on, the beaver jumped into the water with him, diving down under the surface and swimming to the very bottom.

'Look at the traps I have set down here,' he boasted.

But the porcupine was in no position to look at anything. He had swallowed mouthfuls of water and was praying to all the good spirits not to let him perish in such a miserable way. His belly filled with the water until it was as big and round as a melon.

The beaver chuckled maliciously and did not come up to the surface for some time; when he did so, the porcupine was already half dead and ready to give up the ghost. The beaver laid him on the grass, limp and almost lifeless.

'I never thought that a mighty creature like you could come to harm in the water,' he said scornfully, but he was quick to jump back into the pool just in case the porcupine recovered and sent a few of his quills into his coat.

The porcupine lay there moaning and spitting out water and thinking of revenge. 'You wait, you fat old rascal!' he said to himself. 'I'll soon wipe that smirk off your face!'

He limped home, going so slowly that he only got there as night fell. But next morning he was again his old self, and the dawn found him wandering round the pool and wrecking all the beaver's dams, one after the other, laughing uproariously as he did so.

Before long a bewhiskered head emerged from the water.

'What do you think you're doing?' shouted the beaver, his voice breaking with rage as he surveyed the wreckage.

'Why get so excited?' the porcupine mocked him. 'Surely you're not going to make a scene because of a little thing like this! Look, how terribly funny!' And he rolled a huge boulder down the steep bank so that it fell on top of yet one more dam, which crumbled and was swallowed by the current.

The beaver was beside himself with fury. 'You'll pay for this!' he threatened as he disappeared under the surface.

Now he knew he could never defeat the porcupine by himself, and so he swam to fetch his brothers and sisters, his grandmothers and his great-grandfather; in short, he complained about his grievance to the entire beaver family. And since the beavers always stick together, they did not hesitate but at once set off on the warpath.

The porcupine suspected that his little prank would not be allowed to pass unnoticed, but he trusted his quills to protect him. So he ran from tree to tree quite unperturbed, though he was leaving a trail that not even an owl in daytime could have missed.

The beavers accordingly found it at once and, before the porcupine realised that anything was wrong, they had completely encircled him.

Their war cries filled the entire forest. The porcupine bristled, his quills in shooting readiness, but his enemies had counted on this: they threw blankets over him to prevent him from pricking them, tied the ends with Indian knots to prevent him from getting away, and marched off in the direction of the Great Water, singing in triumph.

'What are we to do with him?' the warriors asked their chieftain.

'We'll take him to a desert island. He'll have to stay there for the rest of his life and will never be able to insult us again. Howgh.'

They did as he suggested. Though he struggled hard, the porcupine was borne off to a little island far from the shores of the Indian country.

There was not another living soul on his island, but the porcupine did not despair. Having recovered a little after his uncomfortable journey he went off, snorting and grunting, to take a look round his new home.

He found that there was not even a single tree anywhere—the island was completely barren. 'I must get away from here somehow or I'll surely perish,' he told himself.

All that night and all next day he reflected on what was to be done, and in the end he found a solution that would probably not have occurred to anyone else: he decided to call in the North Wind to help him. He alone would be able to tame the ocean waves so that they should not hurt the porcupine.

And thus, though he was well aware that the North Wind as often as not did more harm than good, the porcupine faced towards the North and, his voice shaking with excitement, uttered the magic words:

'Xune qasa xune
hun hun hun!'

At once the North Wind came roaring and whistling; the waves became still, and the whole world was suddenly lost in a frosty white mist. The porcupine's teeth chattered — he had never known such extreme cold before.

Then the mist slowly lifted, and the outcast saw that he was saved.

The surface of the Great Water had completely frozen over!

Hurriedly testing the strength of the ice, he set out without further delay on his way back to the Indian country. The ice had covered the snowdrifts, and every few steps the porcupine would fall into one. He reached the shore only just in time, for the ice was already beginning to thaw.

He had forgotten all about his feud with the beavers, but when he climbed up to his cave he discovered that his dwelling had been destroyed and his snug lair, in which he had hoped to rest, had been thoroughly wrecked.

'This is really too much!' he cried.

And that very night he assembled a huge army of porcupines, as well as a few hedgehogs who volunteered to help.

The beavers had not been idle either. Their spies had already informed the chieftain about the porcupine's return, so that by the time the dawn came two great armies stood facing one another, ready to do battle.

They were only separated by a stream.

Shouting fierce war cries the beavers hurled themselves into the water and launched the attack. Though they were outnumbered, the porcupines managed to drive them back with a shower of quills. Again the beavers threw themselves forward, and again they were turned to flight, the porcupines taking a prisoner — the beavers' chieftain himself.

Having lost their leader, the beavers had no more stomach for the fight; they scurried home and the battle was over.

It now only remains to be told what befell the prisoner.

The porcupines went into a huddle to decide what to do with him.

'Whatever we do, we mustn't kill him,' said the porcupine chieftain. 'That would anger Manitou.'

'Let's put him up in a tree!' suggested a porcupine great-grandfather.

'Yes, yes, a jolly good idea!' they all cried, laughing. And they at once dragged the bound beaver towards a tall pine.

When they got him to the top they undid his bonds and, with much laughter, clambered down again.

The beaver was very frightened, high up in the tree — his head swam, and every time the pine swayed as a gust of wind shook it, he was convinced he would fall down and be killed when he hit the ground.

The porcupines had the time of their lives watching him, and they danced and made merry under the tree until nightfall.

When they had gone home at last, the wind dropped and the tree stopped swaying. Seeing this, the beaver began to think about ways and means of saving himself from his predicament.

'I certainly can't climb down — I'd only crash and be killed. But I have very sharp teeth. Why not use them?' And he began quietly to gnaw the top of the pine.

He gnawed at the trunk all night, cutting it down bit by bit. At dawn only a short stump was left, and the beaver could now easily jump down before taking a last look at his handiwork. Then he disappeared in search of the nearest water, to make sure he would not be caught again and to have a good drink, for his night's work had made him very thirsty.

And that is why the beaver and the porcupine are such enemies. Should you ever come across a gnawed tree-stump, it probably means that the porcupines have again succeeded in capturing a beaver, who had to gnaw away at the tree in order to escape.

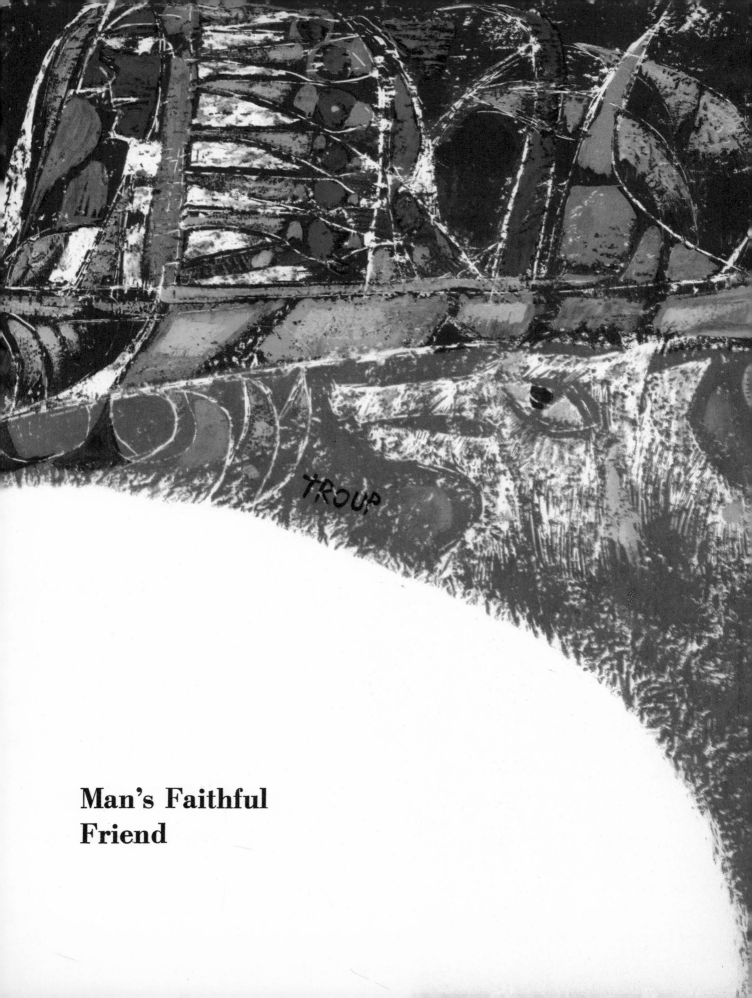

Man's Faithful
Friend

Much sleep had passed in the Lost Valley, many times had Wahu watched the migrating flocks of geese and listened to the thundering hooves of the vast bison herds.

Merciless time had carried everything away on its wings. All that was left were the long shadows slowly settling on the silent countryside. Only they understood the old Indian, and it was with them that he conversed every evening before the stars came out above the camp.

One evening, when the shadows were longest, they brought him a message from the great Manitou himself.

'The Great Spirit awaits thee: prepare for thy journey, prepare for thy journey,' they whispered. 'Make thy farewells, Wahu, make thy farewells!'

'Who is there for me to take leave of?' said Wahu, smiling sadly. 'My sons and daughters have long since left for various corners of the earth, and the people here will be only too glad to see me go.'

The old man rose to his feet. Picking up his battered paddle he walked slowly down to the river.

The silvery mist was already rising from the water when Wahu pushed off for the last time in his canoe. There was nothing now to keep the boat from sailing down the calm river towards the Eternal Hunting-grounds.

And yet had only the old Indian turned to look back he would have seen someone running along the river bank, his eyes full of sorrow.

But Wahu saw no one. Entrusting his canoe humbly to the current, he was carried away faster and faster all the time. And as it was borne swiftly towards the Thunder Rapids, the soft, melancholy melody of Wahu's deathsong sounded above the great roar of the waters.

But someone else had in the meantime thrown himself in the river and was now likewise being carried into the vortex of the tumbling waves.

Wahu fell deeper and deeper, a deafening din drowning all other sounds, until he at last came to rest on a surface as white as milk.

'This is the White River,' he thought. 'Now I shall soon be there.'

Just then he saw in front of him two rocks like a huge gateway, and a bay in which the waves lapped gently in unending succession.

The old man allowed his canoe to drift to the white bank, where he got out. But he had not even taken a good look round when the rocks stood apart and two handsome warriors came out, their head-dress giving off a silvery sheen.

'We are the guardians of the Eternal Hunting-grounds,' said the first warrior. 'We have been expecting you.'

'But why do you come alone?' asked the second.

'I no longer had anyone to look after me, much less to accompany me on this voyage,' Wahu replied.

'In that case, who is it gazing at you from out of the water, his eyes filled with sorrow?'

Wahu turned round abruptly, to find that he was being watched by the most faithful pair of eyes he had ever seen.

'Why, it's my dog! My dog!' he whispered, deeply moved. And he went down to the White River and took his faithful four-footed friend in his arms.

'I would never have thought of him,' he said aloud.

'Yet it was he who loved you best . . .' he heard the voice of the Great Spirit coming from the distance.

Thus it was that the old Indian and his only friend entered the Eternal Hunting-grounds, treading the path along which no one ever returns.

The First War

The calumet finished the story of the faithful dog, and only a thin wisp of smoke now rose from its bowl. The boy therefore asked quickly:

'Did people and animals always get on so well together in the Indian country?'

'No, they did not,' replied the calumet. 'When Manitou gave the Indians bows and arrows and when they learned to make fire, the animals began to hate them, for the hunters drove them out of their old hunting-grounds and stalked them everywhere, their arrows bringing swift death. And, as you have heard, the Indians were then visited by sickness, but plants helped to cure them.

'There was peace between the two camps for a considerable number of sleeps but then the old feud broke out anew. Whose were the hunting-grounds in the Indian country — animals' or Indians'? That was the question asked by the bears, stags and crows, by the opossum and the coyote. And in the end the people took fright and withdrew to the Sacred Rock, where they were able to put up fortifications.

'It was high time! The animals were much stronger in number, and a single herd of bison was capable of stamping out an Indian camp.

'Now they all prepared for war, the birds using trees as drums, the beavers building dams to deprive the Indians of water, and the wolves calling the animal forces together with howls that curdled the blood with fear.

'Yet the Indians were not to be outdone, and they put new strings on their bows and sharpened the points of their arrows.

'And then the war broke out in earnest.

'A huge dark cloud hid the heavens. But no, it was no cloud, it was a vast flock of birds flying towards the Sacred Rock! The bowstrings twanged as they were drawn taut, arrows whistled in the air, there were shrill cries to be heard everywhere, and feathers flew to every side.

'The birds were put to flight, circling for a while helplessly in the air and then flying off way they had come.

'But now came other foes — the prairie was alive with bison and bear, stags and wolves, and foxes. And behind them came alligators, poisonous snakes, lizards.

he Indians ran out of arrows and they quickly made a fire which produced thick, pungent The wind came to their aid, driving the smoke straight at the animal warriors, whose died down. The Indians threw damp wood on the fire, and now nothing moved in the more. The animals coughed and sneezed, tears welled into their eyes, and finally ed the field. The people had won.

ded the first war, but victory did not go to the Indians' heads. And while the sed to give them their flesh and fur, they in their turn swore not to kill any ly and without good reason.'

The calumet stopped speaking. The boy looked at it hopefully — he could go on listening all night, but the magic pipe had gone out and made no more sound.

'I'll put it away, then,' thought the boy. 'It's very late, anyway. Tomorrow we can continue.'

The boy got up from his chair and, putting the calumet in the box in which he kept his greatest treasures, threw a few more logs on the fire.

The wind lashed at the windows but it did not break off the song of the fire; this went on, telling of long-lost trails, of flocks of long-necked geese flying South, of canoes negotiating the wild rapids, of the bygone glory of the Indian country.

THE THIRD EVENING

The boy was consumed with impatience. All day long he had racked his brains wondering what stories the calumet might tell tonight, and when the flowers had closed their cups against the shades of evening he carefully laid the pipe on the table.

But still the calumet remained silent, as if waiting for the fire to blaze up and chase away the darkness; only then did it move, almost imperceptibly. And, accompanied by a light, fragrant scent which rose from its bowl, there came the first whispered words:

'In the glow of their fires the Indians from the forests of eternal snow as well as those from the South and the prairie recounted their ancient legends which I committed to memory so that now, again in the glow of the fire, I can tell them to you.'

'And what will you tell about tonight?' Unable to restrain his curiosity, the boy put the question that had been uppermost in his mind all day.

'I thought you'd ask that,' said the calumet good-humouredly. 'And I know what you have in mind — the famous warriors whose arrows always found their targets and whose tomahawks spread havoc in enemy ranks. But, you know, the Indians never talked much about such as these; it is the pale-faces who write about them in their books.'

'What did the real heroes do, then?'

'First of all they helped other people to lead better lives. And you mustn't imagine that this was an easy thing to do; quite frequently they underwent adventures such as were not dreamed of by even the most celebrated warriors. Or perhaps they might have to use cunning or their sense of humour to achieve their purpose.'

'Like the fox who tricked that coyote?'

'That's right. And now try to imagine an entire army of spirits and evil powers . . .'

'Like witches and dragons and devils?'

'Yes, certainly there were all these. But also evil spirits which took up their abode in the very hearts of the Indians. They were the most troublesome of all adversaries. But enough of these explanations; let me tell my stories.'

Shingebis
and the North
Wind

When the world was still very young, only fishermen lived in it. In summer they sailed in their canoes far away to the north, where there were lakes and rivers exceptionally rich in fish. Before winter set in, however, they always returned home to the South, not wishing to encounter Kabibonocca, the North Wind.

Kabibonocca ruled over the Ice Country, where no grass ever grew, nor did any flowers enliven the white plains. But the Indian fishermen had nothing to fear from him, for Kabibonocca was not master of the whole world. Shawondasee, the South Wind, was stronger than he, and there was eternal summer in his kingdom.

In the spring Shawondasee travelled far to the north in order to help the Indians. The ice on the lakes and rivers melted under his breath, and the way was again open for their canoes. The South Wind had plenty of work to do: first of all it scattered bright-coloured flowers over the meadows, in summer it provided a good maize harvest, while in the autumn it gave the Indians fruit.

When he grew tired, Shawondassee would go to a huge cave in the mountains and there fill his pipe and smoke. Hour after hour the smoke rose from his pipe, and the entire countryside grew quiet and still; there was only the smoke settling slowly like gossamer. The Indian summer was approaching, the loveliest season of the year. But for the fishermen who were fishing in the Far North this 'country full of smoke', as they called it, was a signal to get ready for their return journey. Shawondasee was about to go to sleep and they had to be setting out for home before the wicked Kabibonocca arrived.

And the North Wind was already on his way. He came with long strides and could be heard from afar.

'Kabibonocca's coming!' cried the fishermen. 'It's time we were leaving.' And they all made ready for their long trip down the rivers and lakes.

Only Shingebis remained calm, wondering why they were all in such a hurry. He was a fearless, merry fellow who was not ever put in a bad humour. A big catch would make him rejoice without restraint yet failure did not daunt him, and he always had a joke up his sleeve whatever the circumstances. Moreover, he knew all kinds of magic tricks with which he surprised and confused his friends in such a way that they always had to laugh in the end, even though they may not have found the affair so very funny to begin with. Thus, for instance, he once changed the root of a tree into a snake and roared with laughter when they all fled in panic. Or again, he enchanted their fishing-rods and then pretended to be astonished by their bad luck.

But when he told them that he was not afraid of old Kabibonocca and that he meant to stay there in the North and go on catching fish after they had left for home, they could not understand it at all. Though they knew he was able to change himself into a duck and indeed had every kind of magic at his fingertips, they did not think this would be of much use to him in a contest with the North Wind.

'Kabibonocca is a hundred times stronger than you,' they warned him. 'He can bend even the stoutest trees in the forest. And unless you manage to change yourself into a bear or fish, he'll kill you.'

Shingebis only smiled a tranquil smile.

'Don't you worry about me,' he told them. 'In the daytime my leather clothes will protect me, and at night I'll make myself a fire in my wigwam. Let Kabibonocca just try getting in!'

And while the others loaded their catch into their canoes, Shingebis went on fishing happily. They were all sad when they took leave of him, for none of them believed they would see him again on returning there next summer. But he seemed deaf to all their pleas and entreaties, and so there was nothing left for them to do but to get in their canoes and make off towards the south. Shingebis stood watching them until their boats had vanished over the horizon.

Then he set to work with a will, bringing logs to his wigwam, drying the bark and branches, and then every evening, when the fire sent the shadows leaping and dancing on the walls of the wigwam, he sat there thinking of home and singing. Every morning he went to the lake and fished through a hole he had cut in the ice; and at the end of a day's fishing he invariably returned to his wigwam with a good catch.

Kabibonocca had arrived in the meantime. He drove all the animals to shelter, scattered the prickly needles of snow everywhere, and cut capers with the frost for companion until the trees creaked and groaned. When he at last reached the lake he found there Shingebis returning home with his day's catch.

'Hoooo! Hoooo!' the North Wind cried. 'What man is this, that he dares to stay here long after the wild geese and ducks have flown? Tonight I shall come to his wigwam and put out his fire! Hoooo! Hoooo!'

It was night. Shingebis sat cross-legged by the fire, putting on more logs and contentedly watching the fish as it cooked in a clay vessel.

'They warned me about Kabibonocca, saying he was an evil spirit,' he said to himself, thinking of his friends, 'and that he was stronger than any Indian. Well, I may not be able to withstand such cold as he, but on the other hand, I'm sure he won't like the heat either.'

Shingebis ate his supper, quite oblivious to the noise that had broken out in the forest. Kabibonocca had come roaring up to his wigwam. Thousands of snowflakes fell from the skies but did not reach the ground, for the wind caught them and hurled them at Shingebis's abode. Soon his wigwam was covered with a white blanket of snow which proved useful in protecting Shingebis against the wind and the cold like the fur of a polar bear.

Kabinobocca realised that he had made a mistake, and he flew into a terrible rage. Coming right up to the entrance he began to shout fiercely. But Shingebis was no coward, and he only laughed.

'What's that you're doing out there, Kabibonocca? Look out, or your cheeks will burst with the effort!' he cried.

The wigwam shook under the buffeting of the wind, and the leather curtain hanging over the door kept flying open with a loud sound.

Finally Kabibonocca inflated himself as much as he could, blew the curtain aside, and squeezed in. How chilly was his breath! In a trice the walls of the wigwam were covered with hoarfrost.

Shingebis pretended to notice nothing amiss. He sang quietly, and every now and again got up to put more wood on the fire. It was pinewood, and the blaze was such that he had to sit farther away for comfort. He glanced at Kabibonocca and had to laugh anew, for he saw how the snowflakes and icicles in his hair were changing to beads of sweat; Kabibonocca was slowly melting away: his body disappeared in front of Shingebis's eyes.

'Why, you're trembling all over!' said Shingebis. 'Come and sit by the fire and get warm.'

But Kabibonocca was afraid of the fire. He jumped up and dashed out of the wigwam faster than he had come in.

Outside in the frosty air he managed to recover, and he was again seized with fury. Having failed to defeat Shingebis, he now vented his temper on everything he came across, bending trees and trying to demolish the hide-outs of wild animals. Then he went back again to Shingebis.

'Come on out!' he yelled. 'Why don't you come out, if you're so brave? Let's fight here in the snow, and I'll soon show you who is the master in this Land of Ice!'

Shingebis thought carefully, 'Kabibonocca is sure to have been weakened by the fire and my body is warm, so I can go and tackle him. As soon as he sees I am the stronger of the two of us, he'll leave me alone, and then I can stay here for as long as I please.'

Running out of the wigwam he grappled with Kabibonocca, and a great contest began. They rolled in the frozen snow, only to get to their feet and fall again.

They fought all night, yet still Shingebis did not feel cold or tired: he had warmed himself thoroughly with the exertion and the blood coursed more quickly in his veins. On the other hand he felt his opponent grow weaker and weaker, his frosty breath subsiding and the wind dropping until it was perfectly calm.

With the coming of dawn Kabibonocca saw that he had been well and truly beaten. Screaming with rage he turned tail and fled. He fled far, far to the north, to the northernmost corner of the world. And Shingebis stood in front of his wigwam, singing joyfully, happy that his courage and cheerfulness had got the better of even the fearsome Kabibonocca, the North Wind.

The Wise Hiawatha

The days when Hiawatha was the wise and sage ruler of the great tribe of the Iroquois cannot be remembered by anyone living today. The legend of Hiawatha, however, is still told round the camp-fire, and it goes like this:

In the midst of boundless forests lies the lake Tioto. As if it were today I can see the Indian canoes loaded with meat and pelts, skimming its wind-ruffled surface.

This lake in those days used to be a kind of market-place. It was here that the Indians bartered their game, herbs and fruit, weapons, blankets and other objects. And as at every market-place, there was no lack of noise, argument and bargaining.

When one day they were haggling and arguing as usual, a canoe white as freshly-fallen snow dropped from the blue sky into the midst of their own boats. The shouting and the wrangling ceased at once. An unknown Indian rose to his feet in the white canoe and, scanning their faces, red with rage, asked them:

'What are you arguing about?'

And as if the wind had returned to sigh in the tops of the trees, countless voices again took up the plaint:

'I don't want beaver pelts for my salt!'

'His blankets are full of holes!'

'I can't give good arrows — haven't enough of 'em myself!'

The unknown man raised his hand to silence the crowd.

'Stop acting like a lot of old squaws and listen to me! For I have come to help you.'

No one said another word. All eyes were fixed on the stranger, who continued:

'Go back to the shore and pull your canoes well out of the water.'

The Indians did as he told them, drawing their boats out on to the sandy bank. The stranger's white canoe was among them. Then the unknown man raised his arms up towards the sky.

The Sun instantly clouded and the sky grew black with thousands of ducks, which settled on the lake and began to drink. Having quenched their thirst they flew off again and their place was taken by others; and with more and more flocks arriving all the time,

there soon was not a drop of water left in the lake. Then the birds took wing and disappeared.

'I am Hiawatha,' the unknown man said to the Indians. 'I have brought you money which you can use in exchange for your furs, meat and weapons. Look . . .' and he pointed to the lake without water. On its bottom there lay thousands upon thousands of glittering shells.

'With these you can pay for any goods you need. But first you must chip them and make them round. Then string them like beads and call them *wampum*.'

This was Hiawatha's first deed after he arrived in the Indian country from the regions above the clouds. And since he found living with the Indians very much to his liking, he

stayed with them for good. While the tributary streams and the rain filled Lake Tioto with fresh water, Hiawatha built himself a wigwam on a nearby hillock.

The days and the months and the years passed, and the narrow, hardly discernible path which at first was used by Hiawatha alone had been trodden by so many moccasins that it was now flat and hard like a threshing-floor. This was because Hiawatha's wisdom was known far and wide, and whoever needed advice on any subject under the sun would come to the wigwam by the lakeside to receive it.

There came a time, however, when the stranger's sagacity was to play a really decisive part in their lives. Hordes of fierce enemies from the North swooped down on the lake region, burning down camps, killing defenceless people, and putting whole tribes to panic-stricken flight.

In canoes as well as on foot, groups of desperate Indians came to Hiawatha's wigwam, sitting down on the grass under the trees, as well as in the shadow of the rocks.

Dressed in a long white robe, Hiawatha came among them.

'Your enemies have forced you to flee because you lack unity. Only by linking your forces in a joint endeavour will you be able to withstand them, and there will be a great peace in the Indian country. Behold!' His hand described a wide arc in the air. 'There are so many of you and you all speak a common language, and yet you have never trusted each other. It is only now, with death at your heels, that you have met together outside my wigwam. There is yet time, and if you heed my advice you will be strong—stronger than you have ever been before.'

'We shall gladly obey you,' said the oldest of them all, a white-haired chieftain, rising to his feet. 'Speak, Hiawatha!'

'Very well. Now listen to what I have to say. You, Mohawks, sitting over there in the shade of that huge tree whose roots are fixed firmly in the ground and whose branches are spread wide, you shall be the first nation, for you are fine warriors.'

Hiawatha paused, and then he looked towards another group seated under a mighty tree.

'You, Oneidas, are wise, and therefore you shall be the second nation,' he said.

'I know well the eloquence of the Onondagas, who come from the foothills of the high mountains. For this you shall be the third nation.'

Then Hiawatha glanced at the Indians whose clothes and weapons proclaimed them to be hunters.

'I am glad that you have come here in such numbers, even though your dwellings are scattered throughout the deep forests. You shall join us as the fourth nation, you Senecas — you are fine hunters and must not remain behind.'

Finally Hiawatha turned to the last group of all.

'We know you under the name of Cayugas,' he told them. 'And since Nature saw fit to give you alone the secret of a rich harvest, the Great Spirit Owayneo himself is convinced that you shall become the fifth nation.'

Hiawatha finished speaking. Smiling at the assembled Indians he called his white canoe to him, which then of its own accord, without a single motion of his paddle, sailed away towards the horizon. There it suddenly rose into the air with Hiawatha and, slowly ascending the sacred heights, disappeared for ever from human sight.

Thus runs the legend of Hiawatha, which also tells us that ever since that day the Iroquois — people of the five nations — have successfully defended themselves against all adversaries.

The Adventures
of Manabush

The Indians themselves have never been able to decide whether Manabush was a good spirit or an ordinary mortal. One thing they know for certain, though — that Manabush helped them in every way he could. And that is why there are so many Indian legends about him.

They say he was born many, many years ago, and not even the oldest among the red men remember when it was. His mother, who died when he was still a small boy, was the loveliest of squaws, while his grandmother Nokomis knew the most potent magic; for that reason she was able to live on earth just as in the sky. And it was she who gave Manabush his magic powers.

On that day long ago when Manabush first saw the light of the Indian country, his brothers Chibiabos, Wabasso and Chokanipok were also born.

The legends say that Wabasso did not like the light of day, and so, as soon as he had rubbed his eyes with his puny fists, he ran away from home, going far to the north, to the Snow Country where he became the ruler of darkness and where he lives to this day.

Of his three brothers, Manabush loved the first, Chibiabos, best. This was a kind and merry boy who understood the language of animals and played his magic flute to the amusement of one and all.

However, it was not his fate to please Manabush with his music and his singing for long. One winter day, when Chibiabos was returning home across the frozen surface of the Great Water, the evil water spirits broke the ice under him and pulled him down to their realm for ever. And though Manabush fought them hard, he never saw Chibiabos again. The gay lad remained in the Land of Shadows, the kingdom of the dead.

Just as Chibiabos had been good-natured and gay, so Chokanipok was cruel and wicked. While still a young boy he killed or maimed every living thing he managed to catch. And later, when Manabush went about the world helping the Indians, Chokanipok did the exact opposite. Thus Manabush sent game to the Indians, whereas Chokanipok created all sorts of dragons and monsters to devour it; Manabush gave the people fertile fields, and Chokanipok lost no time in digging deep craters and building steep cliffs.

As Chokanipok's hatred towards Manabush and the Indians increased, so his heart gradually turned to stone. Manabush had long been patient with him, but when he realised that his brother was quite incorrigible he set out after him all the way to the western mountains, and there, after a long and terrible struggle that shook the entire Indian country, he at last defeated him.

After his fight with Chokanipok, Manabush was left alone in the world with only his grandmother Nokomis.

'It is not enough to do good deeds for people,' Nokomis told him one day. 'You ought to travel about the world and gain much more experience. Only then you will be able to advise them.'

Manabush did as his grandmother told him. Going from camp to camp he patiently learned everything the Indians knew, helping them whenever they were in need of advice. Thus he fought and defeated Totoba the owl, who wanted to deprive them of daylight. He taught the hunters to sharpen the points of their arrows, and gave their squaws cauldrons to do their cooking in.

Manabush was very clever, but since he was only beginning to learn things, it often happened that he paid dearly for his experience.

One day he was standing on the banks of a stream underneath a great, spreading tree, gazing down at the water. It seemed to him that he could see in it some lovely red cherries. He reached out for them, but the tempting fruit was too far away. As he leaned over a little farther, his foot slipped and he fell into the stream. The water rippled and the cherries vanished. It was then that Manabush discovered that the cherry tree actually grew on the bank and that what he had seen was the reflection of its fruit-laden branches in the water of the stream.

'So that's how it is!' cried Manabush, clambering up on to the bank and climbing the tree, hoping at last to pick the cherries.

He had reached the crown of the tree and was just about to pick the fruit when he heard a mocking voice calling:

'Got nice and drrrenched, didn't you? Caw, caw, serrrved you rrright!'

Manabush hit out at the jeering crow, but the bird evaded the blow and flew up into the air. His derisive caws could be heard long after he had vanished from sight.

Manabush sat in the tree, having lost all appetite for the cherries. What upset him had not been so much the crow's mockery as the realisation that the bird had only to wave its wings and it was gone. 'I must try and learn to fly too,' thought Manabush. 'No matter if I don't succeed, I'll land on that flat tree-stump over there.'

No miracle happened, and so Manabush fell like a ripe plum. But even the tree-stump proved treacherous, for though quite flat, it was completely rotten, and Manabush crashed right through into a large cavity inside.

'How am I to get out?' he wondered. 'I'll never manage it on my own.'

At that moment he could hear someone approaching. Two old Indian women were walking past the tree-stump.

'I need some porcupine quills to decorate my moccasins with,' said one of them. Manabush heard her and snorted like a true porcupine.

The women stopped and, coming closer, peered curiously inside the tree-stump.

'Do you want my quills?' said a voice from inside.

Astonished, the women nodded their heads.

'In that case dig up the tree-stump with your hoes and then cover my den with blankets so as to keep the wind out. In return I'll stick a few of my quills in them for you.'

The old women could hardly believe their ears; what strange porcupine was this, asking them to destroy his dwelling?

Nevertheless they set to work, digging up the tree-stump and covering the opening with blankets.

'Now go on into the forest,' Manabush ordered them. 'I don't want you staring at me.'

Again the women obeyed him and, as soon as they were gone, he crawled out of his prison and ran like a hare in the opposite direction.

He did not stop until he had reached the shelter of some thick undergrowth, where he burst out laughing at the way he had tricked them.

But he was not to laugh very long, for suddenly his grandmother Nokomis appeared in front of him and chided him.

'You wanted to befriend and help people—why then do you deceive them? You must make amends.'

'True,' agreed Manabush, who now felt very much ashamed of what he had done. 'Please tell me what I am to do.'

'Bring me some strips of birch bark,' his grandmother told him.

Manabush ran to the white trees he could see gleaming in the greenish twilight of the forest and in a moment was back with an armful of bark, which he laid on the ground at Nokomis's feet. She put several of the strips together and skilfully bent them to form a kind of basket; then she took a porcupine quill and used it to link the strips and make them hold fast. She made many more such baskets and, taking one of them in her hands, crossed over to a nearby maple tree. Whispering a few words she pressed the basket to the trunk of the tree, and behold! a thick juice began to drip into her basket.

'Come and taste it,' Nokomis told him. Manabush put a finger in the syrup and licked it. He had never tasted anything as sweet before.

'It's maple sugar,' explained Nokomis. 'Go and tell people it is time for them to get ready their vessels.'

But her grandson shook his head.

'The syrup is too thick and filling. If the Indians were to eat it at once, they would grow fat and lazy, so that anyone could better them. The red men must not live on charity,' he said, and climbed to the top of a tree, where he began to shake the branches.

'Why do you do this?' Nokomis asked him.

'I am shaking the rain-water from the leaves on to the trunk, to make the maple juice less thick. Now the Indians will have to boil it day and night, otherwise they will never have sugar. In this way they'll not be able to grow idle.'

'That is very wise,' agreed Nokomis. 'But now go and teach them everything.'

Manabush went from one camp to another, and wherever there were maple trees the women began to make vessels according to his instructions. When they had filled them with the sweet sap of the trees they made fires, and soon the forest filled with a delicious scent, far more appetising than that of any food hitherto known to the Indians. Their greatest surprise, however, came when the boiled juice had thickened into sugar. None of them, and, in particular, the little children, could eat their fill of this new delicacy.

Manabush visited the wigwams with a smile on his lips, pleased to see that the people were enjoying his gift. In one hut he saw a small child, who was playing on some furs spread on the ground and, quite oblivious to the presence of the mighty Manabush, was happily sucking a stick of maple sugar.

Manabush did not know children, but this little boy had immediately appealed to him. He started speaking to him but Wasis — that was the little boy's name — took not the slightest notice. Manabush began to sing and, when even this proved unavailing, to dance. Still he could evoke no response from the little creature in front of him.

This angered Manabush, and he started to scold the boy, who at once burst out crying and screeching so violently that Manabush had no choice but to stop his ears and flee from the wigwam.

The grown-ups who had witnessed this scene grew numb with horror. How unwise thus to affront the great benefactor of mankind! But of course Wasis was only a child and, instead of trying to appease Manabush, he began to laugh at his panic.

'Gu, gu, gu!' the little boy laughed.

Manabush turned round, not knowing whether to pull Wasis's ears for him or to join in the merriment. But then, since he was a true friend of the Indians, he stroked the little rascal's head and gave him the sweetest piece of sugar he could find.

So much about the kind Manabush and his adventures. The Indians from the eastern forests knew a great many more tales about him, but children like best the one about Wasis, and whenever they're pleased at something they cry 'Gu, gu, gu!' as he did.

Okteondo
and the Wild Geese

Okteondo lived in a deep forest, and since he was a small boy he had his abode among the roots of a mighty elm. But the roots grew and became thicker and thicker, and they twisted this way and that, so that one morning Okteondo woke to discover that he could not find his way out. It was lucky for the little prisoner that his uncle's wigwam was not far away.

Haienthwus looked after his little nephew very well, bringing him food, drink and fruit. Okteondo had only to ask and his uncle provided whatever it was he wanted.

Thus the days went by, with Haienthwus felling trees, clearing the ground round his wigwam, and planting beans and maize, which he then took to the little boy. Okteondo grew big and strong. And though the huge elm did its best to keep him imprisoned, it could no longer do so. When one day Okteondo shook the tree forcefully, the roots failed to grasp the ground again; one more lunge and the boy was free; he stood there in front of his uncle, who had come running from his wigwam and could hardly believe his eyes. Recovering from his surprise, Haienthwus at last managed to speak, and he said:

'So now you are free and, being so strong, I'm sure you will become a splendid hunter. I shall give you a bow and an arrow, and you can go out hunting. Go wherever you please but remember one thing — never turn North! If you do, you will meet with misfortune.'

Though Okteondo listened without saying anything or asking questions, his uncle's words puzzled him and he could not get them out of his head.

He proved to be a fine hunter, having an accurate aim and his moccasins hardly touching the moss, so quietly did he move when out hunting. He soon got to know all the hunting-grounds in the South and the East, and also all the hunting-grounds in the direction taken by the Sun when it rolled into bed at night. And then he again recalled his uncle's warning. Why should he not set out for the North? So many other Indians had been there before him, and all of them returned with plenty of game.

One morning Okteondo came to a decision. Taking leave of Haienthwus as usual, he turned towards the North as soon as he was out of his uncle's sight. His way lay through a huge forest, but he ran from time to time and thus made quick progress. Then the trees grew increasingly sparser and he found himself standing on the shores of a beautiful lake. There was sand on the shore, and the water was crystal clear. A warm breeze faintly ruffled the surface, and far away, in the very middle of the lake, an island sat in the water like a great shell.

Okteondo gazed on spellbound, until at last he was disturbed by someone calling. A dark speck appeared on the horizon, approaching fast and growing larger all the time. Now he could already tell it was a canoe — but what was that skimming the surface in front of it?

Geese! Like so many arrows the wild geese flew just above the water, drawing the boat with its raised prow directly towards Okteondo. The canoe came in to the shore and a strange Indian jumped out, saying:

'Welcome, brother! I am glad to see you. Yes, no doubt you are surprised, but we really are brothers. Haienthwus is my uncle, too. You do not believe me? Come, let us see how tall we are.'

They stood back to back and found that they were exactly the same height — there was not a beaver's hair of a difference between them. But the stranger was speaking again:

'Now show me your bow and arrows. We both got them from Haienthwus, and so they are bound to be the same.'

He brought his out of the canoe while Okteondo laid out his own. Again the stranger

had proved to be right, yet Okteondo still hesitated to believe what he had said. Why had Haienthwus never told him that he had a brother?

'I see you still do not believe me,' the stranger said, watching him. 'We both know how to shoot and we are both good runners. Do you see that tree-stump over there?' He pointed across the bay, to an indistinct black object on the sandy shore. Oktendo nodded. 'Well, aim at it!' Their bow-strings twanged, their arrows sang in the air. 'Come and catch the arrow!'

They ran along the bay, the arrows whistling overhead. Okteondo caught his several feet above ground and, turning round, saw that the stranger was likewise holding his arrow in his hand.

'And now the other way!' Again they put shoulder to shoulder, again they bent their bows taut, again the arrows whistled in the air, and again they both caught them before they had time to land. Okteondo came up to the stranger and said:

' We really are brothers. What is your name?'

'They call me Shagowenotha. Haienthwus did not want to let me go north, and yet here you can have as much game as you wish. Do you see that island?' His hand pointed to the middle of the lake, and Okteondo nodded. 'There stands my wigwam. Come.'

They got in the canoe, Okteondo pushed it away from the bank, and the geese fell into formation as if at some secret command. Shagowenotha began to sing:

> '*Fly, birds, over the lake.*
> *My canoe leaves a silvery wake,*
> *As for the wooded isle we go,*
> *Where we'll sit in camp-fire's glow.*'

The louder he sang, the faster the birds flew, thrashing the water with their wings so that it foamed and the canoe rose almost out of the water. Soon they landed on the island. In the glowing twilight everything seemed a little sinister to Okteondo, and he was glad when Shagowenotha showed him into the wigwam. Okteondo fell asleep at once and did not know that his brother slipped out at midnight and did not come back until just before dawn.

In the morning Shagowenotha led Okteondo to a deep bay, on whose bottom could be seen a large piece of flint.

'You see? This is where I come to play,' Shagowenotha told him. 'Let's try and fish out that stone.' Saying this he undressed quickly and plunged into the water. The stone remained where it was and Shagowenotha swam to the surface with a crestfallen expression on his face.

Without waiting to be told, Okteondo jumped in as well, but this time Shagowenotha did not follow him. Seizing his bow and arrows and his clothes, and putting on his moccasins, he called the geese and vanished beyond the horizon before Okteondo returned to the surface.

The boy searched desperately for his brother all over the island. Suddenly he heard a muted voice crying, 'Okteondo! Okteondo!'

There was no one to be seen anywhere.

'Come here, Okteondo!' the voice called again. And now Okteondo saw that someone's nose was jutting out of a large sand dune. He came closer, and the sand moved, revealing the head of an old man.

'I too am your uncle, Okteondo. Shagowenotha is in the service of a cruel ogre, who will be here at any moment. If you value your life you must hide in the sand like me. But that is not enough. The ogre has a huge dog with eyes the size of Indian shields. You must kill the beast, or it will kill you. Here, take this magic tomahawk. When the dog approaches, all you have to do is to say "Up and at him, little axe!", and you will soon be rid of him.'

At that instant jagged lightning came out of a clear sky, a fierce wind began to blow, and mighty waves came pounding on the shore, one after another.

'Hurry, hurry!' cried the old man.

Okteondo grasped the tomahawk and concealed himself in the sand. Before long everything grew perfectly quiet again, and an enormous dog with a mouth like the entrance to a wigwam and eyes like a couple of shields ran on to the sandy shore. When he came right up to Okteondo's hiding-place the boy called out:

'Up and at him, little axe!'

The tomahawk jumped out of its sheath, leaped into the air, and the next moment the ogre's dog lay dead on the sand.

'Don't leave your shelter!' the old man warned Okteondo. 'If the ogre catches sight of you, that will be your end!'

The ogre was not long in coming. He was big and black and rugged like a huge rock, and crooked tusks protruded from his mouth. He was enraged—shaking his ugly head, making threatening gestures, and uttering strange, rumbling imprecations. He picked up the dead dog and vanished, accompanied by the sound of distant thunder.

Okteondo breathed a sigh of relief.

'Be careful,' the old man advised him once more. 'The ogre will be back in the night because he will have grown hungry by then. We must get away from the island before he comes back.'

'But we have no boat,' said Okteondo.

The old man nodded sadly. 'Yes, you're right. The ogre is very powerful. We'll never manage to escape.' Just then a familiar song came from the water:

> '*Fly, birds, over the lake.*
> *My canoe leaves a silvery wake,*
> *As for the wooded isle we go,*
> *Where we'll sit in camp-fire's glow.*'

It was Shagowenotha coming back. Okteondo and the old man quickly hid themselves in the sand again. The wicked brother jumped out on shore and ran to his wigwam. He wished to make sure that Okteondo was dead, and he was looking for a trail of blood. That was just what Okteondo was waiting for. No sooner had Shagowenotha disappeared from view, than he and his old uncle got in the canoe and made off as fast as they could go.

Shagowenotha searched the island in vain. Okteondo seemed to have been swallowed up by the earth. Angry and worn out he returned to the bay, where a fresh surprise was in store for him. His canoe was gone! Now Shagowenotha knew where Okteondo had gone and he stood there cursing him and trembling for fear of the ogre.

Thunder could be heard approaching the island — the ogre was on his way. There came a flash of lightning, and the ogre stood there in front of Shagowenotha, his angry eyes blazing like two embers.

'Now I have caught you at last!' he shouted. 'And I'll eat you!'

Shagowenotha whined like a whipped dog, crawling about on the ground in front of the ogre and trying to convince him that he was not Okteondo. But his hunger and fury made the ogre blind. Grasping hold of Shagowenotha, he shook him violently — and a moment later his devoted servant had vanished in his gullet.

In this way the wicked brother met his just punishment.

In the meantime Okteondo and his uncle had reached the shore of the lake.

'There's one more thing you have to do, Okteondo,' said the old man. 'Not far from here in the forest the ogre has imprisoned your sister. Before he gets back you must run to his wigwam and set her free. You're a fine runner, and the Moon will show you the way. Go at once and hurry!'

Okteondo set off like a swift arrow along the path lighted by the pale glow of the Moon, and soon he reached his goal. His sister, who had given up all hope of rescue, could hardly believe her eyes. He took her by the hand and together they hurried back. Then they and their uncle got into the canoe, and Okteondo began to sing:

> '*Fly, birds, over the lake.*
> *My canoe leaves a silvery wake,*
> *As for my native wigwam we go,*
> *Where we'll sit in camp-fire's glow.*'

And the wild geese flew so fast that it seemed that the ogre could never catch up with them, no matter how he tried.

When he saw what had happened, however, he looked so intently into the distance that his eyes burned a trail through the dark and he saw the fugitives. Taking his largest fishing rod he attached to it his stoutest line and, aiming carefully, cast it after them. The hook caught the prow of their canoe, which began to glide back to the island as the ogre reeled in his line. They were almost back at the shore when Okteondo remembered the magic tomahawk.

'Up and at it, little axe!' he cried, and the tomahawk jumped out of its shield and with one blow cut the line to set them free.

But still the ogre refused to be cheated of his prey. Seeing that his strength was of no avail he knelt down and began to drink the water. He drank and drank, and the water in the lake kept dropping until the canoe came to be right in front of the ogre's great maw. At the last moment Okteondo grasped his bow and shot an arrow at the ogre's stomach, whereupon all the water ran back into the lake again.

'Now I'll destroy you!' the monster roared, breathing out a frosty gust of wind on to the lake, which at once became covered with ice. The canoe and the geese were held fast by the ice and could not move. The ogre started towards them, running across the frozen surface. As he approached their boat, the wise old man rose to his feet and muttered a magic formula. The ice at once began to melt. Before the ogre could touch them the ice gave way under him, and he disappeared under the surface, never to be seen by human eyes again.

The three fugitives were saved. Soon they reached Haienthwus's wigwam under the big elm, and there they lived happily and in unity until the day the Great Spirit called them to him.

And what about the geese? Okteondo released them and gave them their freedom. But they did not separate, and even today they can always be seen flying together in arrow formation, and the Indians, looking up at the sky, know that the wild geese are migrating.

Wihio
the Wanderer

When Wihio was born, his restless fairies gave him a taste for travel and a merry disposition as his christening presents.

He was not in the least sorry about this, especially when he discovered that the life of a wanderer was far more interesting than the lives of those who never left their teepees, and that a great deal of fun could be had while travelling.

As soon as he had learned to handle bow and arrow Wihio ran away from home, walking boldly in the direction of the huge forests which showed blue below the snow-capped mountains far to the north.

There were so many sights to be seen here that his eyes, used to the flat prairie country, hardly knew where to turn first. There were swiftly flowing streams which leaped over everything that stood in their way, sunny forest clearings, tall pines whose crowns were so high you could hardly see to the very top.

Here lived many animals Wihio had never seen before, and he at once started talking to everyone he met. Thus he learned much forest wisdom, getting to know, among other things, that the animal chieftain here in the North was an awesome big bear, who kept jealous guard over his rich hunting-grounds by the Bear River and sent everyone packing who trespassed on his territory.

But Wihio would not have been Wihio if he had not played some trick on the big grumbler.

It happened in winter. Wihio reached the frozen Bear River and, quite regardless of the proximity of the bear's den, he cut a hole in the ice and started catching fish. Before long he heard behind his back a heavy footfall and angry noises, but Wihio pretended not to notice and, calm as you please, went on pulling one trout after another out of the hole. The bear flew into a great rage.

'How dare you to come here and catch my fish!' he roared.

Wihio looked up at him and smiled amiably.

'Ah, here you are at last. I've heard you only use your paw to catch fish and that consequently many get away. And so I've come to show you what to do to gain a catch that is worthy of you. Now look!'

Wihio put fresh bait on his hook and threw the line into the water. In no time at all he had caught such a fine specimen that the bear's mouth watered just looking at it.

'That's all very well,' he complained. 'But I have no fishing-rod.'

'Never mind,' replied Wihio. 'You have a fine, fleshy tail, which any fish will be only too happy to bite into. Do you know what? You stand with your back to the water, put your tail in, and as soon as you feel the fish bite, just pull it out quickly.'

'Well, I suppose it's not a bad idea, but I warn you — don't try playing any tricks on me, or it will go ill with you!' the bear said, shaking a heavy paw in front of Wihio's face. And without more ado he squatted at the edge of the hole.

Soon he felt something catch hold of his tail. Waiting a little longer, to let the fish bite properly, he jerked it up, but found it would not come. His tail stuck fast in the hole.

'Come and give me a hand!' he called out to Wihio. 'I've caught a big one!'

'Don't be such a fool!' cried Wihio, laughing boisterously. 'You haven't caught anything — your tail has frozen in the hole. Serves you right for being such a selfish beast!'

Gathering his catch and putting it in a sack, Wihio strolled slowly away, whistling a song about a stupid bear.

The bear shouted and tried to wrench himself free, but still his tail stuck to the ice. He had to summon all his strength and then — crash! he rolled over and fell to the ground. His tail was almost gone, only a very short stump remaining in its place. He really had been taught a lesson.

Wihio wandered on, leaving the snow-covered forests and reaching a country of red rock and deep gorges. All the Indian villages hereabouts were empty.

Why was this? he asked himself, and he soon heard the reason. A huge owl reigned over this territory, and as she was in the habit of carrying off little children during the night, people had moved to safer parts. Wihio at once made up his mind to seek out the wicked bird, but no one could tell him where to find her.

Consequently, Wihio dressed up as a little child and waited for the owl to come for him.

Exactly at midnight he heard an owl's hooting, and then the swish of mighty wings. Suddenly he was grasped by a pair of claws and swept up into the air.

They did not fly very long, for the owl had her nest in a rock hollow not far away, and this is where she carried Wihio. She was very pleased with her prey and, letting go of him when they had reached the nest, she boasted:

'No one can vanquish me, and you'll never leave here alive. I'm looking forward to the fine meal you'll make!'

Wihio acted as if this did not concern him in the least; reaching inside his sack he pulled something out of it and began to eat, smacking his lips.

'What have you got there?' asked the owl, craning her neck inquisitively.

'A piece of maple sugar. Would you like a bit, too?'

'Give me the lot!' ordered the owl imperiously.

Wihio again put his hand inside the sack, but this time, instead of the maple sugar he was himself crunching, brought out some soft pitch. The owl suspected nothing and started to eat it. Finding it difficult to get down, she clamped her beak vigorously in order to munch it up, but she soon found that was a mistake. The pitch glued her jaws together, and Wihio walked out laughing.

When he was outside, he started to sing again, adding new words to his song of the stupid bear, which told of an even more stupid owl.

The owl was still beating furiously with her beak against the rock when Wihio was far and away, having arrived in a country of swamps and bogs. Little did he guess that this was the domain of the most terrible of all alligators.

By the time he found out, it was too late. A huge maw, like the entrance to a wigwam, opened before him. Another step and Wihio would have been lost.

'Come, come!' the alligator urged him on in an unpleasant, grating voice. 'You can't get away, whatever you do.'

'Had I seen you first, I should have devoured *you*,' Wihio told him.

The alligator laughed.

'That's a joke! I'd like to see you do it!'

'Oh well, what's the use of talking about it now? I'm sure you're the mightiest of all animals. But since I am to part with my life, at least show me your teeth, so I can see what is in store for me.'

The alligator felt flattered. Opening his mouth as wide as it would go, he stuck out a red tongue. This was just what Wihio wanted. He pulled a large stone out of his sack and threw it in the alligator's mouth to prevent him from closing it again. Then he quickly cut off half of his tongue.

The alligator shouted and sighed and groaned with pain and rage, for he could not get rid of the stone in his mouth.

In the meantime Wihio wandered on. The song he hummed this time told about the reason why the alligator has only such a short tongue.

He travelled for several days, by the end of which time he felt thoroughly hungry. But though he looked everywhere for something to eat he could find nothing.

When at last he met a coyote he rejoiced, for he was sure that this cunning rascal would know where to look for some delicacy. He therefore stopped him and said:

'How now, brother, you seem very well fed to me. Tell me where one can find some good food.'

The coyote was at first reluctant to tell him, but in the end he said:

'Well, all right, listen. There is a teepee below that hill over there, and it's full of the finest dried meat you can imagine. I feasted there a number of times, but then they thrashed me with a stick, calling me a thief and brigand. You'd better not show your face inside it.'

Thinking this over, Wihio realised that the coyote was probably right; whoever lived in that teepee was evidently a miser and did not want to share his meat with anyone else. But then he had a good idea.

'Now you listen to me,' he told the coyote. 'I'm going to dress up as a woman and put you in my sack, which I'll carry on my back. You must wail like a hungry child, and you'll see they'll not fail to give us something to eat.'

The coyote listened carefully, and then he scratched behind his ears.

'Well, it's going to be pretty hard work for me. You must promise only to taste every bit of meat we get and leave the rest to me.'

Knowing that otherwise the coyote would refuse to help, Wihio promised to do as he asked. There would be plenty of time to see what could be done about it later.

So, wasting no more breath, he stuck the coyote inside his sack, tying it up so as to leave only his eyes protruding. Himself he disguised as an Indian squaw, tied the sack to his back as the Indian women did with their little ones, and went up to the teepee below the hill.

Sitting inside was a man.

'Why does your child weep so?' he asked.

'It's very hungry, and I have nothing to give it, for I myself have no food,' Wihio replied in a high-pitched voice.

The man took a few pieces of dried meat and handed them to Wihio without a word.

The meat was delicious. Wihio enjoyed it very much, giving the coyote, who by this time began to move and grumble in the sack, nothing but the bones and tough bits he could not eat himself.

Thanking the man for his gift, he left the teepee and made for the river.

The coyote was furious.

'You wait till I get out! I'll give you a good hiding for cheating me like this!'

Wihio paid no heed to the coyote's threats, but, taking the sack down, threw it into the water.

He stood there a few moments and then, sitting in the green grass, his eyes followed the sack as it was carried downstream and he composed another verse of his song, this time about the coyote, the most stupid animal of them all.

The Purple Swan

There was once a chieftain who had three sons. Shortly before he died he called them all to him to bequeath them his only legacy. When they came in he sat up for the last time on his bed of furs and, facing the Sun, which was setting in the west, he spoke to them in a faint voice:

'My eyes are weak, and I know it is time for me to depart for the Land of Shadows. But before I leave on my long journey, I want you to take this as a gift from me.'

The old man put his hand under the furs and brought out a long quiver decorated with porcupine quills. Handing it to the eldest of his three sons he said:

'Inside there are three magic arrows. Keep them and look after them well. They were given to me by my father, a celebrated warrior, who in turn received them from his grandfather, who was the most famous of arrowsmiths. And now leave me, for I wish to be alone.'

The next day the old chieftain set out on his journey to join his ancestors. The whole village mourned him, recalling his brave deeds and wise decisions. But, as is the way of the world, in time they forgot about him, and only the three brothers would visualise his face as they sat together over the three magic arrows.

One evening the youngest of them, Ojibwa, went out hunting. He had no sooner left the camp than he came across a fresh track of a bear, and he followed it. Ojibwa was a fast runner, and he managed to catch up with the animal and kill it before the Sun went down. As he was skinning his prey the sky flamed purple and a strange, melancholy sound issued from the spot where the colour was most intense. It was as if the wind were playing upon a magic harp.

Ojibwa stopped working and looked in the direction of the alluring voice. Throwing aside his knife, he started to run through the forest, led by the purple glow.

He ran a long time until he found himself on the banks of a large lake. And on it, just at the place where the blue surface of the water joined the fiery sky, he saw a purple, long-necked swan. It was the swan who sang, and the strains of her haunting melody affected him deeply.

'You must be mine!' he cried, stretching his bow taut. But all his arrows went wide, as if misdirected by some magic.

Ojibwa wondered what to do. Then he thought of his father's legacy, and he ran quickly back to the camp. In his wigwam he picked up the three magic arrows and hurried back again to the lakeside, his feet hardly touching the ground.

The purple swan seemed to be waiting for him. Ojibwa shot the first arrow, but it landed too near. Nor was he luckier with the second, which only grazed the bird's plumage and fell on the surface. The third arrow went home, but it did not kill the purple swan. With a mighty flutter of her wings she sailed majestically into the air and vanished in the gathering clouds of evening, her haunting song dying in the silence.

It was some time before Ojibwa recovered from his enchantment to realise that the swan had carried away his precious arrow.

'I must find it and bring the arrow back, or my brothers will curse me to my dying day for having lost our father's legacy,' he said to himself, and he recovered the other two arrows from the lake. On one of them he found a purple feather from the swan's wing and he carefully put this away before starting out on his quest of the unusual bird.

He walked and ran all night and all the next day, until at last he came to an unknown Indian village. The chieftain himself welcomed him, and his daughter, with a face as lovely as the glowing morn, watched over him while Ojibwa slept soundly till the first light of dawn. Early in the morning she gave him a new pair of moccasins in place of his own, which he had torn to shreds the day before, and she accompanied him a considerable distance out of the village to show him the way.

Ojibwa ran the rest of that day until nightfall, when he saw before him the silhouettes of wigwams of another Indian camp. Here, the chieftain welcomed him, his daughter watching over him all night and at dawn presenting him with a new pair of moccasins. And she, too, saw him a good part of the way, being sorry to let him go, for she had grown fond of him and secretly wished he would stay with them for ever.

And again Ojibwa ran on and on, until that night he saw a light shining in a lonely wigwam. Going in, he found there an unknown old man who greeted him in a most friendly fashion.

'I have been expecting you a long time,' he said. 'I know well who you are and where you are going. You're searching for the purple swan. She lives one sleep away from here

with her father, a mighty magician. He once lost his scalp while fighting his enemies, and since that day has been condemned to undergo great suffering which will not cease unless a brave and clever young hunter can be found to bring his scalp back to him. Let me tell you moreover that the purple swan sings in such a melancholy way because she pities her poor father. But all those she lured with her singing before you have perished.'

'I am not afraid,' Ojibwa told the old man. 'I'll go and bring the magician's scalp back for him. I am convinced that my spirits will not abandon me.'

The old man nodded his head.

'I sincerely hope you will succeed. But remember what I now tell you. Tomorrow morning you will already hear the magician's lamentations. Beware, however, of looking at his scalped head in daylight — only if you do so in the glow of the fire shall you escape unscathed. Should you see the magician in daytime, you would go mad with horror.

'And when you try to get hold of the scalp, don't forget the swan's feather . . .' the old man added mysteriously.

Ojibwa thanked him for his advice and, having eaten a little, slept well and long. In the morning the old man woke him and accompanied him along the way until they heard the magician lamenting.

'And now you must go on alone. Do not forget what I have told you, and delay your steps,' the old man warned him before vanishing in the gloom of the forest.

Ojibwa obeyed him, and it was evening before he entered the magician's wigwam. There he saw a man sitting by the fire and lamenting. A look at his head made Ojibwa shiver with horror, and he took a step back against his will. Yet, the thought of the purple swan imbued him with such courage that he advanced again and bravely asked:

'Please tell me where I can find your scalp, for I should like to help you.'

'Who are you, that you are not terrified to look at my face?' the man asked him, fixing his eyes on the youth. 'No one has been to offer me his help for a very long time now.

'My scalp was carried away by my enemies to their camp, which lies three sleeps away from here in a northerly direction. If you bring it to me, I shall return your magic arrow and reward you in a way you would not expect in your wildest dreams.'

'You can rely on me,' replied Ojibwa. 'I shall start on my way at once.'

It took him a full three sleeps before he at last saw the smoke above the wigwam roofs and heard human voices. He stopped and looked vigilantly about him. Seeing sentries posted all round the camp, he realised he would never get through in his normal likeness and he thought of the purple swan's feather. Stroking it gently, he was at once changed into a kingfisher.

Now he could inspect the camp at his leisure. The wigwams stood in a circle, in the middle of which there were some poles, and on the highest of these hung the magician's scalp.

He flew towards it and was about to seize the scalp when the Indians noticed the brightly coloured bird and began to loose their arrows at it. The kingfisher dropped a purple feather from his beak, and the feather floated down to the pole, attached itself to the magician's scalp, and then both were carried by the wind to the nearby wood, where Ojibway was already waiting, having in the meantime taken on his human form again. And before the Indians had realised what had happened, he was well away in the forest on his way back to the magician with the scalp.

'Put the scalp on my head, and I shall reward you,' the magician told him when he had arrived. And when Ojibwa did as he asked, he suddenly found himself facing a tall, handsome man, whose eyes were smiling kindly at him.

'You have done a great thing for me in returning my scalp and thus enabling me to regain my manly appearance. I shall never forget it. Here is your magic arrow. And now enter my wigwam and take your reward. It is my only treasure, but I shall be happy for you to have it.'

Ojibwa entered the wigwam. There he stood as if rooted to the spot, for in front of him he saw the fairest maiden who ever walked the Indian country. The stars might well have envied her her sparkling eyes, a rose would have been proud of the red colour possessed by her lips, and her legs would have made even a doe jealous.

'I am the purple swan,' she said. 'My heart belongs to you for having helped my father. If you wish, I shall become your wife.'

Of course Ojibwa agreed. Before night fell he and his bride said goodbye to the magician and started on their journey home.

Ahayiute
and the Cloud-eater

On the sunny side of the Indian country there towered a huge mountain which from a distance resembled an ear of maize. For this reason the Indians called it Maize Mountain.

It was there, on the very summit of the mountain, that Ahayiute and his grandmother had their dwelling. He led the same sort of life as other Indian boys, and probably would never have got into this story if he had not one day felt a longing to do something that would make him a man and a warrior.

At first sight it might seem that there was nothing easier for Ahayiute than to fulfil his wish; for he was as swift as an antelope, as agile as a trout, and as strong as a bison, so that he was a match for anybody. But time passed with the slow-flowing stream of the Lazy River, and while many other boys of his age had already become men, Ahayiute was still waiting for his opportunity. He used to come home dejected and gloomy, and as often as not would hardly touch his food.

'I know what ails you,' his grandmother told him one day. 'And I also know how to help you. But I fear it will be a task you cannot accomplish. . . .'

'I am no coward,' replied Ahayiute, 'and that is just the kind of task I have been waiting for.'

'Very well, then, listen to me,' said his grandmother, lowering her voice, so that the boy had to draw nearer in order to hear her words.

'It is a long time ago now that the Cloud-eater settled in the East.'

'The Cloud-eater?'

'Yes, that's right. He is as tall as the Maize Mountain, and he can open his mouth so wide that it stretches from one end of the horizon to the other. He feeds on the clouds, and that is why we get so little rain, and both people and animals often die of thirst.'

'And has no one ever defeated the Cloud-eater?'

'Many brave men have set out for the East, but not one has returned.'

'Well, I am not afraid, and I shall fight the Cloud-eater.'

'As you wish, but it will be an unequal struggle. The only thing I can do to help is to give you these four magic feathers to take with you,' said his grandmother, taking four feathers, each a different colour, out of a wooden chest.

'If you put the red feather in your hair, it will lead you straight to the Cloud-eater,' she explained. 'The blue feather will help you to understand the language of animals. The yellow feather has an even greater power — it can make you so small that you will be able to enter a mousehole. As for the last feather, the black one, that will give you the strength you will need for your encounter with the Cloud-eater.'

Ahayiute asked no more questions. He put the four feathers away carefully, and before the birds had finished a single song he was ready to start on his way. Taking leave of his grandmother, he put the red feather in his hair, and very soon he had left the Maize Mountain far behind.

Ahayiute travelled East all the time until he reached the Cloud-eater's kingdom. Here the land was arid, the grass completely dry and withered, and in places there were dead trunks of trees. Life seemed to have become totally extinct. Only a little mole peered inquisitively from his molehill, blinking at the newcomer.

'Gowa!' Ahayiute greeted him, taking out the blue feather. 'How shall I get to the Cloud-eater?' he asked in the mole's own language.

'It is only a few sleeps distance,' the mole replied. 'But beware: as soon as the Cloud-eater sees you, you are the son of Death. Look—' and the little creature pointed to the barren countryside. 'All this is his handiwork. He has destroyed every living thing, and I myself only escaped because I happen to live underground.'

Without another word Ahayiute stuck the third feather in his hair, and he at once grew smaller until at last he was no bigger than the mole.

'Now I can pass through your corridors,' he said. 'The Cloud-eater shan't see me, and I can reach him without difficulty.'

'Well, I can see you're not only brave but also cunning. None of your predecessors thought of asking my help, and they all perished. I shall gladly show you the way.'

Ahayiute bent over a little, for the underground passage was still a little too low for him, and he followed the mole, treading cautiously while his eyes grew accustomed to the dark in the tunnel.

They stopped only to rest and eat. The mole had large stores of food spaced out along the way, and the boy was only sorry that he could not cook his meals, for the mole disliked the flames and, in particular, the smoke.

All of a sudden the path began to twist and turn, and the mole said:

'We're under the Cloud-eater's wigwam. Listen and you will hear the earth tremble.'

Several large stones fell into the passageway, and the walls shook violently.

'The Cloud-eater is asleep and is rolling about,' explained the mole, quite undaunted by the terrible earthquake. 'We must go on a bit farther.'

They reached the very end of the passage, which grew wider now and led them to a large room.

Ahayiute straightened up, but then he again quickly lowered his head, as the ceiling was regularly pressed down almost to the ground. Loud, hollow knocks could be heard coming from above.

'That's Cloud-eater's heart beating,' whispered the mole. 'You would have to be very strong indeed if your arrow were to reach him.'

Ahayiute now took out his last feather, the black one, and at once felt the strength of a man and a warrior coursing through his veins. Then he straddled his legs, put the sharpest arrow to his bow, and aimed at the spot where the ceiling bent most of all.

Drawing the bowstring taut, he let loose his arrow. There came a terrible roar that shook everything all round them. The last thing Ahayiute saw was the ceiling as it collapsed on top of him . . .

When he came to, he was lying in the grass and the mole was wiping his forehead. A little way off lay the motionless serpentine body of the monster.

'You're a brave fellow! You did it!' cried the mole delightedly. 'In his death throes the Cloud-eater showered us with stones, which knocked you out. But I dug a new corridor and brought you out above ground. Look there,' he added, pointing to the Cloud-eater. 'He's dead. Your arrow pierced his heart. He'll not torment anyone any more!'

Ahayiute looked up at the sky. Rain clouds floated quite low, bringing moisture to the countryside, as well as the message that Ahayiute had just become a fully grown man.

Shavenis and the Water of Life

Shavenis was a poor young girl who lived with her parents in the smallest dwelling of the *pueblo*. Hunger and want were their constant companions, and, therefore, when she grew up, Shavenis wondered what to do to drive them away. She knew that neither her mother nor her father were strong enough to work, and that she alone would have to carry out her plan.

'I'll pick cotton and teach myself to weave,' she said to herself one day, and before long she had made a big loom.

First she wove a pair of the beautiful stockings the Indian women wear for the festive dances. Then she made herself a lovely white dress, *manta*, and finally she made an attractive sash.

The whole *pueblo* marvelled at her skill, and all the women longed to have the same beautiful things as she had.

Shavenis was pleased when she was asked to sell the things she made. She wove an even lovelier *manta*, which she also sold. 'I don't mind, as long as I get a good price,' she thought.

Thus after a time every woman in the *pueblo* had a brand new dancing outfit, for Shavenis went on weaving without stopping. And the more such lovely dresses she made, the greater grew the vanity in her heart. She was now not only rich and beautiful but also proud and unkind.

Girls of her age were just then beginning to get married. Shavenis, too, was sought after by the Indian youths, who came one after the other, as is the custom in the *pueblo* to this day, bringing her their wedding gift — a fine white robe they had woven with their own hands.

But Shavenis refused every one of them.

'I don't need your gifts!' she mocked them. 'I can weave clothes too, and better than you can weave!'

The older people watched pride taking hold of the girl's heart, and they nodded their heads sagely.

'You are not doing right, Shavenis,' they told her. 'The good spirits have given you wealth because your heart was kind. Now it is full of pride, and such people are always punished. . . .'

'Stop talking such nonsense!' she retorted angrily. 'If I feel like it, I shall buy the entire *pueblo* and drive you out of here!'

From that time no one again dared to warn her, nor did any more youths think they could make her their wife.

There was still one, however, who could not forget her beauty and who, day and night, went on weaving the most beautiful wedding gown for her. This lad was called Scarface, because his face carried scars inflicted by the sharp claws of Tumwa the bear.

When the wedding robe was finished, the youth took it to Shavenis.

'What brings you to me?' the girl wanted to know.

'I trust in the goodness of your heart, Shavenis, and have therefore brought you my wedding gift,' the youth told her, about to show her the robe.

'Pshaw! You needn't bother! Others have been here before you, and I chased them all away. Surely you don't think I'd spend my life looking at your mutilated face?' was the girl's cruel reply.

The boy dropped his eyes and departed in silence, deeply hurt by her words.

Scarface did not tell anyone about the way he had been insulted, but Shavenis herself saw to it that everyone learned about it.

That was her last wicked deed.

When night came to the *pueblo* — a stifling, starless night, whose stillness was only broken now and again by the eerie howling of a dog — the darkness in the room in which Shavenis slept seemed to tremble all of a sudden, and three strange apparitions approached her bed. Only their unusual, soft voices betrayed their presence.

'I gave her beauty and health,' said the first voice. 'In return for her wickedness I shall send illness to her!'

'I gave her wealth. She does not deserve it and must lose it!'

'She is wicked and heartless,' whispered the third spirit. 'Unless her heart is cleansed of pride, she must die! Howgh!'

None of them spoke again, for at the last word lightning flashed from the heavy clouds, and before its glow had waned the three apparitions had climbed up it, as up a ladder, to the starry *pueblo* in the sky.

A violent storm broke, the thunder waking people from their sleep; and then it began to rain.

Shavenis knew about none of this. She slept soundly till morning, and when the Sun sent its rays against the white walls, she opened her eyes. She wanted to get up, but a strange drowsiness seemed to bind her limbs so that she was unable to move. She tried to call her aged mother, but her tongue was heavy and wooden, and she could not speak.

Now she realised she was ill.

She lay there a long time, helpless and still. It was almost evening when her mother came at last. Seeing from the expression on her face that her daughter was ill, she at once sent for a magician to come and cure her.

The magician at first showed little inclination to do so, for he liked Shavenis no better than the rest of the villagers, but when he was offered a large sum he took his medicine and went to the girl's bedside.

He spent the whole night there, lighting a number of fires in the room and putting on them various vessels in which he boiled herb potions, muttering incantations all the time.

Shavenis obediently swallowed all the medicines he gave her, but still she felt no relief. On the contrary, before night was out she heard for the first time the voices of the dead calling her to the Land of Shadows.

In the morning the magician took his reward and left.

'My medicine is mighty,' he said in parting. 'Yet it cannot cure the illness which has afflicted Shavenis. Since you have been so generous, I want to give you some good advice. An even more powerful shaman lives among the rocks in the mountains, and if you give him all your wealth, he will surely cure the girl.'

Her parents did not hesitate for a moment, and they called in the other magician.

For three whole days and three whole nights the old man tried to drive the illness out of the girl's body, but to no avail. The only thing he succeeded in doing was to return the gift of speech to her, so that she was able to say:

'For the third night in succession I have heard the voices of the dead in the Land of Shadows calling me. They keep growing louder, and I fear them. Tell me, wise magician, must I really die?'

The shaman shook his head.

'My medicine could not help you, though there is no mightier than it anywhere in the Indian country. I know of a remedy, but I doubt . . .'

'Oh, do tell me, magician, and I'll give you all I have,' pleaded Shavenis.

'I see that the illness has driven out your pride; that is a good sign. But for health to return, you need love. And you have chased away all those who wished to give it to you.'

Shavenis burst into tears, bitterly regretting her past behaviour and wishing she might make amends.

At that moment they heard a ladder creak outside as someone ascended it to enter her room. It was Scarface, the boy whom Shavenis had hurt most of all.

'I have heard it said that you are mortally ill,' he told her. 'I can hardly believe it. But I am sure you will get well soon.'

'No, I shan't get well,' replied Shavenis gravely. 'I shan't get well, because I only loved myself.'

'Would you like to help her?' the magician interrupted them.

'Yes, indeed,' replied the boy. 'I still love Shavenis, even though she hurt me so very cruelly.'

'In the desert a long way from your *pueblo* there is a stream of the Water of Life,' said the magician, lowering his voice. 'You must find it and bring the water to me at once. Take my jug — the water will never dry up in it.'

Scarface took the shaman's jug and prepared to leave.

'Wait,' the magician stopped him. 'Remember that your efforts will only be rewarded if you genuinely love Shavenis, otherwise you'll never find the Water of Life.'

For three days the young man wandered in the desert, but nowhere could he find any trace of the stream mentioned by the magician. All he saw was dune upon dune of hot sand. Many a time he thought he had found it, but always he was to discover that it was merely a mirage.

On the third day he was so tired that he dropped down on the sand and fell asleep. He dreamed of the beautiful Shavenis, who was smiling at him and singing a lovely song that reminded him of the babbling of a distant brook.

At that instant he woke. Jumping up, he found nothing but the desert all round him; there was no sign of Shavenis, yet he could still hear the murmur of water, even more strongly than before.

Then he realised the stream must be underground. He began to remove the top layer of sand until he had dug down to stone. He despaired of ever getting to the water, for he was now very weak. Then, when he had rolled away a huge boulder, a powerful column of water gushed out of the ground. As soon as he had washed his face in it he felt revived and strong; and, what was more, the water had completely healed his scars so that not a trace of them now remained.

Filling the magician's jug with the Water of Life, he hurried back to the *pueblo*.

Shavenis was dying. She had already become resigned to the idea that the youth had failed to find the magic spring and that she would have to leave this world. All she now wished was that she might be granted a last look at Scarface, that she might take leave of him before she died. Thus when he came in she lifted herself in bed and was about to speak her last — but instead the youth gave her a drink out of the magician's jug.

Shavenis recovered after the very first sip. Getting out of her bed she looked gratefully at the lad who had saved her life. Only then did she notice that the scars no longer marred his face.

'Yes, he too was helped by the Water of Life,' the magician told her, advancing towards the young couple. And, turning to the boy, he said: 'I know how well Shavenis loves you, and I believe you will be very happy together. But you must never permit pride to find a way into your heart again.'

And with these words he turned away and left the house.

The Story of Niagara

Since time immemorial the waters of the Niagara have been falling into the deep gorge, its thundering stream swallowing up everything it manages to catch hold of. And yet the Indians who know Niagara — who hear the rumble of the waterfall on their long voyages, by the fire, as well as in their sleep — are not frightened of the Niagara. That is so because they know this story. . . .

There once lived a beautiful maiden in an Indian camp. Many good, brave, and daring young men tried to woo her, but her parents in the end gave her to a bad-tempered but wealthy old man, who tormented and beat her. She did not even get enough to eat but had to work from sunrise to sunset, while the greedy old man only piled up and jealously guarded his *wampum.*

No wonder, then, that the girl wept wherever she went. Several times she tried to run away from him, but always the old man caught her again, and she was then even worse off than she had been before.

'I'd rather be dead than suffer like this any longer,' she said to herself one day.

It was evening, and the hunters were just returning home in their canoes. The girl watched them go ashore, and when she saw that there was no longer anyone about, she quickly jumped into one of the boats. The current carried her straight to the waterfall, where suddenly the water dropped away as it tumbled down into the precipice. The canoe fell like a plummeting stone, and the girl closed her eyes, expecting her end. But to her great astonishment the canoe, instead of hurtling down to hit the surface with a terrible crash, came to rest lightly, as if caught by some giant hand.

The girl found herself in a huge cavern, its entrance shut off by the waters of the great waterfall.

'Paddle towards me! Paddle towards me!' she heard a kind voice calling her, and she at once lost her fear. Looking in the direction of the voice she saw a man so huge that his little finger was as long as her canoe.

'Who are you?' she asked.

'I am Hinun, the good giant, and I wish to help you. Niagara told me you were coming. You can live here in my abode until the selfish old man dies.'

The girl was only too happy to stay in the giant's cave, and she indeed lacked nothing there. Hinun told her about everything that happened in the camp, telling her how the old man looked for her in vain.

One day, however, he returned home with a frown on his kind face.

'Your husband is a very wicked and greedy man,' he told her. 'To get as much *wampum* as he can, he is buying fire-water from the pale-faces and selling it dearly to the Indians. He knows only too well how harmful fire-water is to the red men, but he cares nothing for that, all he is interested in is amassing more and more riches.'

'What will you do about it, Hinun?'

'I must measure my strength against his,' the giant replied, and he was gone before she could put any more questions to him.

The old man sat on the floor of his wigwam, gloating over the large heaps of glittering *wampum*.

'My lovely shells, my beautiful shells!' his bloodless lips murmured. 'There are still so few of you!'

He was so engrossed that he failed to notice that a snowstorm had broken outside. It was only when the wind leaned violently against the walls of the wigwam that the old man sat up.

'What's happening?' he whispered, seized by a feeling of dread.

There came a clap of thunder. The greedy old man ran outside, and there he stood face to face with Hinun. The giant's face was red with anger.

'I have come to punish you for all your misdeeds,' he said threateningly.

'Ha, ha!' the old man laughed derisively. 'You've made a mistake, Hinun. The evil spirits are stronger than you!'

Raising his arms above his head he began to wave them about like a pair of wings, muttering unintelligible words as he did so.

His face suddenly went black and turned to stone; his arms and legs, his entire body became stone at the same time.

The stone monster stepped forward. The ground trembled beneath him, and in vain did Hinun shoot arrow after arrow at his body.

'Ha, ha! Your arrows cannot harm me!' exulted the horrible creature, breaking the arrows in two in his stone fingers.

Hinun turned and fled, pursued by the old man. With one single leap the giant reached the rock above the waterfall and began to climb. Again the old man followed him. Hinun stood up on the very top of the cliff, his head touching the dark clouds. But his adversary had caught up with him and began to push him towards the precipice. The giant resisted him with all his might, but gradually he weakened and was forced to the edge. Only when he was actually leaning over the drop, feeling the fiery breath of the stone monster scorching his skin, did he wrest free of the deadly grip and jump aside. The old man also tried to avoid falling, but the edge of the rock could not bear his weight and it crumbled into bits under him.

A great roar echoed among the rocks as the old man fell, his stone body breaking into many pieces. The evil spirits who had up till now protected him, turned tail, lamenting, 'Oh-weh! One of us! Oh-weh!' And the echo carried their wails all over the countryside: 'Oh-weh! Oh-weh!'

The girl waiting in the cave also heard the news. She could hardly wait for the giant to come back, and when he arrived she told him:

'I know that you have defeated the greedy old man, and I shall never forget what you have done for me. Now I think I should return home, but perhaps you would be kind enough to help me get across the waterfall.'

'Get in the canoe,' Hinun said and, when she had done so, picked the canoe up in one hand while he stopped the waterfall with the other so that it should not harm her, and he set the boat down gently on the bank.

'You need no longer fear your husband,' he told her in parting. 'And should anyone ever wish to hurt you again, let him go and look at the rocks.' Glancing back for the last time, the giant entered the tumbling waters of the Niagara and vanished in them forever.

The girl looked round her. Perhaps it had all been but a dream, she thought. But no, here was the path leading back to the camp. There, she failed to find her husband, and when she and the others went out to the rocks they could see with their own eyes what had taken place. Everywhere there lay scattered large black stones, strangely reminiscent of a human body.

'So this is all that has been left of the wicked old man,' the girl said, recalling the giant's words. 'Let these stones be a warning to all Indians who might desire riches and great wealth.'

How the War Tomahawk was Buried

A wise chieftain once lived in a certain village. He had fought in many battles, and it was common knowledge that he was the strongest and bravest of all warriors.

One day he watched the children playing merrily in front of the wigwams. What would become of them when they grew up, he wondered. The boys would probably grow into fearless hunters and brave warriors like himself; yet, which of them would live to a ripe old age so that he could use all his acquired experience and turn it to benevolent wisdom? No doubt they would win victories and gain many scalps, but many of them would in their turn be vanquished and scalped by the enemy. And what about the girls? They would become the wives of warriors, and many would die a long way from home. Perhaps they would be granted some little happiness, but then cares and age would write on their faces, on which would appear deep wrinkles of sorrow as they would remember their husbands and sons who had died on the war-path.

Thus the chieftain reflected day and night. And he came to realise that the Indians were not born to fight and die, that what they really wanted was to work in peace. This gave rise to a great idea, and he accordingly called a meeting of the whole tribe.

When they had all assembled, the chieftain rose and spoke to them about wars that had never brought any good to the red men. He spoke of the scalp hunters, who attacked lone warriors only to acquire one more trophy.

'The first Indian who ever lifted his tomahawk against his brother was a bad Indian,' he said. 'And even though the taking of scalps has become second nature to us, there is no reason why we should continue with it, for it is a bad habit.'

Thus spoke the wise chieftain, and the others saw that he was right. And they decided not to paint their faces and set out on the war-path unless they were themselves attacked by others.

'But who is to carry the message of peace to the neighbouring tribe?' they asked.

'Silent Moccasin and Swift Stag,' replied their chieftain.

These were two handsome young Indians, the fastest runners of the whole tribe. Their eyes glowed with pleasure when the chieftain told them what he wanted them to do, and they lost no time in preparing for their journey.

And early next morning, as soon as the first rays of the Sun had touched the pine-needles littering the ground of the forest, the two young friends ran out of the village, all of whose inhabitants had come to see them off.

Soon they came to a large wood. Though it was a clear, sunny day, not a shaft of light penetrated the thick foliage. Fallen tree-trunks, thorny bushes and swamps barred their way. But the youths did not give up; one changed himself into a wolf and the other into an owl, and now they managed to overcome every obstacle. Having at last reached the nearest Indian village they took on their human form again and buried their arms.

Their arrival created a stir in the village, and all but the sick and aged ran out to look towards the forest, at the edge of which stood two of their worst enemies. But since the young men carried no arms and their faces were not painted, they allowed them to pass unmolested right into the middle of the village, where they handed the astonished chieftain the peace message of their tribe. The chieftain heard them out, and said:

'I like the proposal made by your people; it is my proposal too. But before I give you my reply, I must consult my warriors. In the meantime I want you to be my guests.'

While he had been speaking, his braves began to gather round, and almost all of them gladly agreed to install peace in the Indian country. Only a few, in whom love of battle had clouded both heart and brain, stood out against the suggestion. But even these were silenced by the decisive words of their chieftain:

'I know only too well what war means. If all the tears shed by Indian women for their lost husbands and sons were poured together, they would make an ocean of sorrow; if the blood shed by the warriors combined in one stream, all our brooks and rivers would turn red and overflow their banks. If only our men trod the path of the hunt instead of the war-path, hunger and want would never find a place in our camps. War means ruin, destruction, and death. This is the wisdom I have gained after many years squandered on the war-path. Let no one think, therefore, that I am a coward if I send the following message to our neighbours: I, the chieftain of my people, accept every word of your proposal. Let us meet four days hence halfway between our two camps in the big meadow by the river.

There we shall dig a pit, and in it we shall throw all our war weapons. Then we shall shake hands and live like brothers for all time.'

Silent Moccasin and Swift Stag were well pleased to hear these words; and then, after the fairest of the village maidens had presented them with new moccasins, they set out on their return journey.

The joy with which they were welcomed home defies all description. For three whole days the Indians waited impatiently for the great moment, and on the morning of the fourth they all gathered in their finest clothes in front of the chieftain's wigwam and, singing and dancing, made their way to the big meadow. A deep pit had been dug in the middle, and on the other side of it they could see the people from the neighbouring village.

The chieftains were the first to step forward. Both threw their war tomahawks into the pit, clasping hands like brothers. All the others now followed their example, and when the last had cast away their arms, the joy of the entire gathering knew no bounds. Men and women, boys and girls danced together, the happy lilt of their songs echoed by river and forest.

Not even the Sun felt like going to bed that day; as if unwilling to leave this happy scene, it lingered long amidst the evening clouds, smiling down on the rejoicing Indians. Then at last it closed its eyes blissfully and rolled over on to its golden bed beyond the horizon. But that happy smile it has retained to this day.

The Secret of the Calumet

'My stories are at an end,' said the calumet, breaking the profound silence that had settled after its last words.

'Why so?' asked the boy. 'You haven't yet told me anything about the Indians fighting the pale-faces.'

'I only remember the tales I heard at the camp-fire while peace still reigned in the Indian country. The ships of the pale-faces did not arrive until many, many sleeps later. Then even the tranquil place where the mountains meet the prairie and the snow-covered forests join the arid desert, even that tranquil place where I rested guarding the camp-fire, was suddenly transformed. Hundreds of Indians fled this way, all of them making for the West. One day I came to understand why, for a cloud of red dust appeared on the horizon. This time it was not the bison, whose herds I had so often seen galloping past before. These were soldiers on high horses — the army of the pale-faces! They stormed across the camp like a tornado, calling to each other in a language I could not understand. And then something even stranger took place. An Indian came out of the nearby forest. I wanted to shout to him to drive these intruders out, but before I could do so one of them stopped his horse, put a long rod to his face, as if taking aim, and then it happened: a tongue of fire shot out of the rod, there was a loud report, and the Indian at the forest's edge fell dead.'

'That was a rifle, surely!' cried the boy.

'Yes, I know that, too, since that day. I did not see any Indians for a long time afterwards. Their camp had been destroyed, and it seemed to me that their fire would never blaze again.

'But I was wrong. One foggy night I was awakened by a familiar glow and by voices speaking a language I could understand. A number of Indians were sitting round the fire, debating. Then one of them found me.

' "Look, there is a calumet," he said. "It must have been Manitou himself who sent it to us. Let's take it along."

'The Indians took me with them, and it was then that I had my great adventure . . .'

'Oh, do tell me all about it, please!' the boy entreated.

The calumet paused, deep in thought.

'If I do that, I shall crumble into dust, for I shall have told a human being my greatest secret. But I have told you all the other Indian tales I know, and I am sure you will pass them on to other children. Therefore listen to the last tale of all.

'The Indians carried me about with them wherever they went, and it was anything but a pleasant journey, for Death lay in wait for them everywhere — Death meted out by the long rifles of the pale-faces.

The Indians were cold and hungry, as there was no time to go hunting and they could not make fires for fear of betraying their whereabouts. Thus many women and children died, and so did many of the most famous warriors — Hawk Eye, Whistling Arrow, Red Cloud, Silent Moccasin, and many, many more.

One day I thought the exhausted Indians had come to the end of their path. Tall, impassable mountains towered ahead, and all round, with their fingers on the triggers of their rifles, stood the white soldiers in a circle so dense that not even a mouse could hope to slip through.

When that night the Moon lit up the red faces, the chieftain Last Smoke rose to his feet and said:

'Tonight a bloody Sun set beyond the hills. I fear that this is a bad omen, by which Manitou means to tell us that tomorrow we must expect to put up our last fight, and that we shall be defeated.

'We know we are in the right, and we shall fight like men for our Indian country against the pale-faces who want to take it from us, as well as to deprive us of our freedom.

'Nevertheless, the knowledge that we were in the right has never yet helped us. We welcomed the pale-faces like brothers, and they repaid our hospitality with fire-water, which befogs the mind of the Indian, and with diseases which annihilated whole camps and villages. But worse was still to come. The pale-faces started taking our hunting-grounds from us, which have been ours since time immemorial. They are driving us from place to place, and we are defenceless against their weapons. Let us go no farther, brothers. If we are to die, let it be tomorrow, fighting man to man. There is one thing that saddens me, though: what will become of our women and children? Our enemies will not spare their lives in battle. Perhaps it might be better to give ourselves up in the hope that the heart of the white men will soften at the sight of defenceless, helpless people.'

When the chieftain had finished speaking, an Indian by the name of Big Scout got up and said:

'I was sorry to hear the words uttered by Last Smoke, not because they were not wise. True, our bodies are weary with this endless journeying and our souls are full of sorrow at the thought that we are never again to return to the land of our forefathers which was our home.

'Last Smoke has rightly said that we are still free, and he wants us to go out tomorrow and fight. We all know what an unequal struggle it would be. And to rely on the white man's mercy if we throw away our arms? No, that would mean to spend the rest of our days miserably in stone houses — forts and jails they call them. I myself have been locked up in such forts *a number of times, but thanks to my silent moccasins I was always able to slip out past the guards and regain my freedom.*

'Well, why not do that now? I have wandered all over the Indian country in my time and I know every corner of it. These parts are no exception — I know of a secret path over which we can escape. I shall lead you out of this encirclement and we'll keep on going until we find a spot in this country of ours from which no one will ever drive us again. Howgh!'

Big Scout's speech left a deep impression in the minds of all the Indians. That very night, as soon as the Moon had hidden behind the hilltops, they left their camp and passed through the chain of white sentries, following the secret path Big Scout had told them about.

I remember how I then found myself in a canoe; the Indians had reached Old River and were making their way south down its stream. Yet not even there did they find hunting-grounds on which they could settle down and live in peace. The pale-faces hounded them everywhere, and it was only due to Big Scout's skill and knowledge that they always managed to escape, though often this seemed almost a miracle. They travelled all over the South, carried me across the Snow Country; they passed through the region of canyons and lakes and got as far as the Thundering Waterfalls, but still their enemies were at their heels. And as the years went by, there were more and more pale-faces in the Indian country, whereas the Indian fires went out one by one. Only Manitou knows how many empty camp-sites I saw in those years, how many uprooted totems and scattered hearths. And only Manitou also knows how Big Scout, together with a handful of brave Indians, tirelessly went on looking for a place where the white man had not yet penetrated.

Sometimes indeed he thought he had succeeded. Under his command the Indians won the famous battle of Lost Creek, and they were able to stay there, living in peace for several months until the familiar screech of the Army bugle one morning forced them to move on once more.

The path led on, and soon the Indians who followed it were one by one called to the Land of Shadows by the voices of their dead ancestors.

Thus it came about that Big Scout said farewell to the dying Last Smoke and continued his unending journey alone. All he had left was his bow and arrows, and myself.

Again I saw lakes and rivers, and the limitless prairie. Then Big Scout arrived once more at the place where the mountains join the prairie and the snow-covered forests join the hot, arid desert.'

The calumet grew silent.

'And there?' asked the boy.

'And there Big Scout left me. But before he departed, he spoke to me thus: "I shall go on wandering through the Indian country until this world comes to an end, looking for a place in which the red men might live in peace and happiness. When I find it, I'll tell about it to the

trees in the forest, the grass in the prairie, the water in the streams, rivers and lakes, the stones in the mountains and in the valleys, to the Sun and the darkness and the stars in the sky, the clouds and the winds, and I shall ask them all to give my message to my people."

'Howgh!'

Saying this, the calumet vanished in a whiff of smoke. The boy jumped forward to the table, waiting for the smoke to disperse. But instead of the calumet, all he saw in the dim glow of the crackling fire was a heap of reddish dust.

'So that was the secret of the sacred calumet!' he whispered, thinking of the pipe's last words to him.

Taking his treasure-box, he carefully put in it all the dust that remained. And as he held the fine reddish particles between his fingers, he felt that each of them was telling him once more one of the legends he had heard from the magic calumet over the past three evenings.

American Indian Tales and Legends

When the night wind played in the crowns of the bare trees and the snow fell ceaselessly on the bark wigwams, the Indians, old and young, would meet together to listen to wise men telling stories.

The red men were no less proficient at this than story-tellers anywhere else in the world. And, although in their tales knights did not triumph with the aid of magic swords, although they did not tell about mighty kings and pious hermits, they did speak of beings endowed with magic powers, these being most frequently animals.

Why animals?

The North American Indians lived in the open, and they were mostly dependent for their food on the wild animals they managed to kill. They knew how to find the animals' trails, when to expect the wild geese and the bison herds, but they were at a loss to explain these recurring phenomena in any satisfactory way. They believed therefore that Nature must consist of many invisible beings — spirits — who were ruled, as were they themselves, by the most powerful spirit. This Great Spirit was called different names in the individual regions — names such as Manitou, Tirawa, Wakonda, Cipas, and so on.

Some animals and spirits were friendly towards people, others were not. One such friend, according to the inhabitants of the Northeast was Manabush (Manabozho, Nanabozho, Manavabush, etc.), whose name in fact stands for Big Rabbit. This Manabush mostly appears in their tales as a human being, becoming a cunning fellow whenever he assumes his animal form. Trouble can be expected when that happens, and it is he himself as often as not who finds himself in it.

From the prairie regions, all the way across the Rocky Mountains to California, stories are told of the coyote, a kind of distant relation to Manabush, who used his powers chiefly to spoil all the good things that existed in the world in legendary times.

The best-known fairy-tale creature in the North-west, however, was the raven. He, too, was cunning and crafty, like the coyote, having the additional propensity to greediness. His cawing was considered an evil omen by the Indians, and for that reason the raven in their tales usually represents evil.

The Indian belief in the supernatural powers of animals was reflected in the fact that they considered animals to be their ancestors, and their own names were frequently derived from the animal world: Swift Stag, Little Wolf, and so on.

This belief in animals is expressed in superstitions, myths, legends and fairy-tales — but there are also the carved and painted totem-poles of cedar wood which used to stand in front of every dwelling and which, in Northwest Indian villages, formed entire totem groves. The heads and bodies of animals — protectors of the clans — as well as the most important events in the history of the tribe were depicted on them.

The Indians came to the root of many natural mysteries: thus they knew how to kindle fire, cure various diseases, protect themselves against cold, and so on. But until the coming of the white men's civilisation, they still explained away most natural laws and phenomena by means of legends and stories, which have come down only by word of mouth, passed on from generation to generation.

Numerous Indian tribes lived in North America, and they differed widely in their way of life, as can be seen from their tales.

Thus, for example, the Indians of the north-eastern woodland lived by hunting wild game, and they lived in huts called wigwams (the Abnaki name for home); since theirs was a region full of lakes and rivers, they also used canoes made of birch bark on their travels. The heroes of their legends possess magic arrows which never miss, moccasins which lead their owners in the right direction, magic canoes which can float in the air like birds —in short, everything these hunters would have liked to have themselves.

The Indians of the Southeast liked to hear stories about animals, and they preferred humorous tales. Their greatest hero was the rabbit, who was by far the cleverest of all and got the better of everyone: of the wildcat and the coyote, as well as the fox. The same region also has some very fine legends about maize, tobacco, and curative herbs.

To the west of the Mississippi, also known as Father of Rivers, there are endless plains which were once the home of the prairie Indians. They, too, lived by hunting, especially by hunting the buffalo, whose flesh they ate and whose skins provided them with almost everything they needed: clothing and vessels, as well as their cone-shaped tents which they called teepees.

In the East the Indian wigwams were built deep in the forests, where their inhabitants could only rarely glimpse the star-studded night sky; but the prairie people saw thousands of stars glittering overhead every night. They therefore thought a great deal about them, asking themselves how they had reached the sky, and why some of them travelled while others remained stationary. They imagined them to possess human faces, just as the Sun and the Moon; and they gave expression to their notions in legends about the universe.

Some of the south-western Indians lived in pueblos. These were terraced dwellings which could be reached only by means of ladders. And though this may have had its drawbacks, it was certainly very much an advantage when there was an enemy attack to be feared, for then the pueblo became a veritable fortress.

The pueblo dwellers, too, found an explanation for various natural phenomena in the activities of supernatural powers and spirits, whom they called katchinas. And since down there in the Southwest they often suffered droughts, the life-giving rain plays an important part in their legends.

The Indians of the north-western coastal areas, as opposed to their brethren elsewhere, had real cedar-wood houses, and they lived by fishing. They used nets and wicker baskets to catch the migrating river salmon, and they set out to sea in narrow canoes, armed with harpoons to match their wits against the whale.

They had their totem-poles, and also a remarkable ceremony called the potlach, which was attended by guests from near and far, being linked with a big feast and the exchange of gifts.

The ocean had its part to play in their fairy-tales. The whale, the salmon, and the thunderbird were frequent heroes, not to mention the fearless fishermen with their harpoons.

Our list would not be complete if we omitted the Indians of the extreme Canadian north, who are close neighbours of the Eskimoes. They hunted the caribou, using snowshoes and toboggans to get about in a country that was under snow the best part of the year. The tales and legends of these northern Indians often speak of cold and hunger —two constant foes with whom they had to contend.

And now all that remains is to answer the question why it was the calumet which narrated all these Indian stories.

The calumet was one of the most sacred objects the Indian knew. Its ash-tree tube was painted in symbolic colours and adorned with eagle feathers, and its carved bowl was made of red steatite.

The Indians considered the calumet to be a kind of altar, using it as a mediator when asking the spirits for their favour and expressing their gratitude. The calumet also played a major role at their counsels and ceremonies, and particularly in their peace talks with enemy tribes. That, of course, is why the calumet is also known as the 'peace pipe', a beautiful designation which has remained alive to this day.   V. H.